PULSE OF THE PLANET

PULSE OF THE PLANET

EXTRAORDINARY SOUNDS FROM
THE NATURAL WORLD

By Jim Metzner

THE NATURE COMPANY

The Nature Company owes its vision to the world's great naturalists: Charles Darwin, Henry David Thoreau, John Muir, David Brower, Rachel Carson, Jacques Cousteau, and many others. Through their inspiration, we are dedicated to providing products and experiences which encourage the joyous observation, understanding, and appreciation of nature. We do not advocate, and will not allow to be sold in our stores, any products that result from the killing of wild animals for trophy purposes. Seashells, butterflies, furs, and mounted animal specimens fall into this category. Our goal is to provide you with products, insights, and experiences which kindle your own sense of wonder and help you to feel good about the world in which you live.

Pulse of the Planet was prepared for publication by Elliott & Clark Publishing, Washington, D.C.
Designed by Gibson Parsons Design
Photo editing by Annie Griffiths Belt
Photo research assistance by Dolores Metzner
Printed in Hong Kong through Mandarin Offset

The Nature Company staff:
Douglas Orloff
Catherine Kouts
Anni Lazarus
John Luckett

To order this book or learn the location of The Nature Company store nearest you, call 1-800-227-1114, or write The Nature Company, P.O. Box 188, Florence, Kentucky 41022.

ABOVE: BOOMING SANDS, NAMIB DESERT.
PAGE 2: INSIDE LEMON CREEK GLACIER, ALASKA. PAGE 5: MUSIC OF THE DUMJE CEREMONY, NEPAL.

CONTENTS

PREFACE

How often are we given the chance to listen to something we've never heard before? That, in short, is the opportunity this CD presents. It offers a myriad of unusual sounds from around the world, collected during the 20 years that I've been producing radio features, including over 1,400 "Sounds of Science" and "Pulse of the Planet" programs.

Many of the recordings on this CD, including *Arctic Ice*, *Atmospheric Whistlers*, and *Elephants*, were made by scientists in the course of their research. Other sounds, including *Booming Sands*, *Termites*, and *Oropendola Bird*, were gathered by that intrepid, devil-may-care, endangered species known as the "sound recordist." These misguided souls actually take pleasure in braving ridiculously harsh conditions for the sake of committing a few vibrations to posterity. I've had the honor of working with some of the best field recordists in the world while producing the radio series and this CD.

There are indeed some remarkable ambiences in this collection—memorable both for how they sound and for what they represent. Of course, one affects the other. The appeal of *Cosmic Background Radiation* is enhanced enormously when you learn it's the oldest vibration in the universe. The sounds of *Lava Flow* are surprising, yet they lead the listener to a visceral understanding of volcanic phenomena. *Siberian Shamans* are among the earliest anthropological field recordings ever made. Recordings of tornadoes are understandably rare; ours is simply the best—and the scariest—I've ever heard.

Having listened to and lived with these sounds for years, I feel that each of them possesses a quality that eludes description. Perhaps that's why they were recorded in the first place. On rare occasions in the field, one has the sense of being at a crossroads, as a unique sonic moment unfolds amidst the generic "wash" of the soundscape. Someone else might close his eyes and listen, or write about the sound, or let it go. But for some reason, my colleagues and I have been given the chance to preserve these rare moments by simply turning on a tape recorder.

Later, a generation removed, that recording will have a life of its own. Then comes the impulse to share the sound with others, hoping that it won't lose its magic in the process. The question is, what will enable you, the second generation of listeners, to hear it deeply? What mysterious combination of words, pictures, and silence will allow you to have your own unique listening experience?

This album of exotic sounds is meant as an offering of unprocessed "ear food" for those curious about the natural world, and to anyone interested in exploring and rediscovering the magic of listening. —*Jim Metzner*

Jim Metzner and dolphin, California.

9

LEVELS OF LISTENING

He who sleeps in continual noise is wakened by silence. —WILLIAM DEAN HOWELLS

There are very few places on earth that are absolutely quiet. One is a manmade environment called an anechoic chamber, or "dead room," in which any noise is instantly absorbed by the soft textures and uneven surfaces of the walls, floor, and ceiling. To most of us, used to living in a melange of sounds, spending any time in such a room would be an uncomfortable experience: *dis*-quieting. It may even be that the normal human neurological system *needs* a daily dose of sound stimulation.[1]

In fact, we are bathed in sound, and moved by it—literally. At a concert you can feel the low frequencies of a bass instrument resonate deep in your chest. Higher frequencies are more subtle, yet move through our bodies as well. Hum a low tone with your lips lightly closed, and you'll feel the vibration on your lips, as well as your jaw, throat, and chest. Change the tone to a higher pitch, and you'll sense the vibrations shifting through your body to the top of your head.

Sound also has a powerful effect on our inner state. This will come as no surprise to anyone who has ever heard chalk screech on a blackboard—not to mention pneumatic drills, subway trains, snowmobiles, low-flying aircraft, and neighborhood dogs. Likewise, sounds such as the ocean, rainfall, and certain music can help us relax or even put us to sleep.

Studies suggest that the very act of listening can also have a profound physiological effect on our bodies. Some people experience a marked rise in blood

OPPOSITE: RADIO TELESCOPES LISTENING TO OUTER SPACE, NEW MEXICO.

pressure whenever they speak. On the other hand, the act of listening often causes blood pressure levels to drop.[2] It is a gateway between our psyche and the world we live in and interact with. Our well-being can be influenced by *how* we listen, as well as by *what* we listen to.

Most likely the place you are right now, indoors or out, is full of sounds that you haven't even noticed. These could include the backwash of traffic, bird calls, the hum of a refrigerator, a ticking clock, rain, the squeak of a chair, the rustle of clothing, the rhythm of your breathing. These sounds seem to "appear" as you tune them in, and recede as you tune them out. Is that what listening is, or are there deeper levels waiting to be discovered?

You might try this exercise: imagine yourself at the center of a circle six feet in diameter. Now try to hear all the sounds within the full circumference of this circle. They will include, of course, the sounds of your body—breathing, pulse, ringing of the ears, even your thoughts. Hearing all 360 degrees will be a challenge; we're not in the habit of listening to every sound we hear. Nor do we often concentrate on letting it *all* in. Usually our attention jumps from sound to sound, like a bee flitting from flower to flower. Here, then, is a type of listening that encompasses not one flower at a time, but the whole garden. It engenders

PATTERN FORMED BY SOUND VIBRATIONS.

a sense of being in the midst of a living, moving "sea" of sonic delights.[3]

Most of the time, however, we are forced to choose, albeit unconsciously. Psychologists have been studying our ability to discriminate between different types of sounds, focus on what we want to hear, and disregard the rest. They call this the "Cocktail Party Effect," from the example of someone carrying on a conversation amidst the background noise of a crowded party. If such a reaction were not part of our hearing mechanism, our attention would fall prey to every sound we hear. Imagine a walk through Times Square under those circumstances!

The price we pay for this ability to focus in and tune out is that we tend to have a relatively narrow field of audition. We disregard peripheral sound unless someone in the "front office" of our brain deems it useful, or until a sound intrudes upon our consciousness. To use an example from the world of sound recording, our ear and brain working together tend to function like a shotgun microphone, which picks up the sounds it's pointed at, rather than an omnidirectional mike, which is equally receptive to all sounds equidistant from it. Most of the time, we're in the automatic listening mode, or the sonic equivalent of autopilot.

Automatic Listening

During our lives we've developed habits of listening, just as we've acquired habits of eating, dressing, and virtually everything else we do. Our first act of listening probably took place in the womb, where amidst the sounds of our mother's body, we gradually became familiar with the sound of her voice.[4] Growing up, we quickly learned to interpret the rich and subtle tapestry of sounds that fill our environment. Even before we could speak, we understood the language encoded in our parents' tone of voice. Indeed, we borrowed the sound of their voices as blueprints for our own, tempered by the inflections of a regional and neighborhood dialect as well as our own physiology.

Our voice, unique as a fingerprint, is arguably one of our most personal possessions, the link between our inner and outer worlds. You'd think we'd know its sound well enough by now. Why then do so many people react with surprise or even dismay when they hear themselves on a tape recorder? "Do I really sound like that?" we ask. "Yes, you do," we're told, but why can't we recognize ourselves?

This may be an indication of how subjective our listening really is. No person or tape recorder hears your voice the way you do, as a blend of two sounds—one traveling through the air from your mouth to your ears, the other transmitted conductively from your vocal apparatus through the mass of your head. Yet there's evidence we are strangers to our own voices even without a tape recorder to jar our sonic sensibility.[5]

One reason we don't pay more attention to the sound of our own voice may be that we don't *need* to. My friend and fellow sound recordist Tim Wilson suggests that mankind's listening developed biologically as a test of whether or not a sound represented a threat. From this "antenna-up" mode, we evolved a functional automatic listening that is still, at its root, an early warning system.

This would account in part for why we don't heed familiar sounds,

particularly our own voice. On the other hand, if you're driving a car, an unfamiliar noise is the cue that "something's wrong with this sound picture." For an instant we're jarred out of the automatic mode until we've identified the problem—faulty piston!—and pulled over. Automatic listening, then, may keep us from a deeper listening experience, but it nevertheless delivers an astonishing amount of information.

Consider how much is communicated to us through sound alone, even at the subliminal level. My phone could ring right now. I might pick up the receiver and by hearing just one word, "Hello," know at least four unspoken facts: it's my brother-in-law; he's intoxicated, happy, and far away. We don't know precisely how our auditory mechanism sorts all this out, but it demonstrates that sound can convey many different kinds of information with a great deal of subtlety. We take this ability for granted, along with much of the rest of our listening. Sound continues to influence us, whether we're aware of it or not.[6]

The greater part of our listening is merely reading a road map of already familiar terrain. As a touchstone to our inner world, ordered sound, music especially, has the power to conjure up a lifetime's worth of thoughts and emotions.

THE AGE WHEN HEARING DEVELOPS IN THE WOMB.

15

To movie audiences, a certain sequence of musical notes will always resurrect the *Jaws* shark, while another melody will invariably call forth Miss Gulch on her bicycle in *The Wizard of Oz*. It's no accident that heads of state like to appear in public accompanied by the national anthem. Sound does not enter our inner world unattached; in a very real sense we've "heard it all before."

In fact, our identifying mechanism works so well that the label describing a sound is often affixed before its vibrations have fully penetrated our bodies. Our brains have become so good at identifying what we hear that we substitute the label for listening itself. Whether it's music, the spoken word, or environmental sound, we process it unconsciously; it stays in the realm of the familiar, and our listening goes no further.

Intentional Listening

What happens, though, when we're concentrating on sounds that interest us, be it music, conversation, or—in the case of the compact disk that accompanies this book—pure sound? Obviously, there are degrees of attention—levels of listening—that we apply to sounds we *want* to hear. Anyone who has attended the symphony and tried to pick out a particular instrument has had this experience. The same holds true for a seasoned auto mechanic, who uses his ears to tune an engine. Listening, however, can take us further—beyond the boundaries of what we know or expect.

Consider that in conversation, nothing turns us off faster than someone who tells us *everything*, leaving no opportunity for us to think, come to conclusions, or simply listen. Just as there needs to be room on a computer's hard disk for information storage, there needs to be space in our minds and bodies for listening to take place.

Skillful speakers intuitively know this. Instead of battering us over the head with their message, they let us come to it on our own terms. We're even allowed the thrill of discovery as they lead us to the brink, the frontier, of a new idea and then pull up short, encouraging us to hear or imagine what's been left unspoken. It may or may not be what the speaker had in mind—it might even be an improvement! The point is, there's room for this discovery to take place.

Intentional listening, then, is in part a function of how much "unoccupied space" there is in me at any moment. That in turn depends on how willing I am to give up the first batch of associations called forth from the automatic listening mode. In other words, if I "know it all," there's relatively little or no room for listening.

But if our inner echo chamber quiets down, a higher state of consciousness may be waiting deep within the onion-layers of listening. It's no accident that the great religious traditions place enormous emphasis on sound.

"In the beginning was the Word," states the Judeo-Christian Bible; "Om," intone Hindus, chanting the vibration that created the universe; "Religion is sound," say the Tibetans. The great Tibetan saint, Milarepa, is even depicted with his hand to his ear, listening. In Gregorian Chant, arguably the basis of all West-

ern music, a channel of prayer is opened though which the singers praise God and receive what could be called "divine inspiration."

Cultural anthropologist Donald Tuzin, speaking about the role of sound in religion, reminds us that music can evoke a deep emotion, which he describes as, "There must be a God, otherwise I wouldn't be feeling this way." It may be that this special feeling is touched by, and ultimately associated with, certain forms of music and sound. Indeed, music has been an essential part of the ceremonies, rituals, and celebrations of virtually every religious tradition on our planet.

A "sacred sound" may even have some quality—an inherent order or form—that helps us listen. Upon hearing the chanting of the Gyütö monks (selection #5), a listener described feeling the ascendent harmonic structure of the chord as a series of sensations rising through his spinal column like a sonic totem pole. Even afterwards, when the chanting was over, he could still hear the chord and feel the accompanying impulse to assume an erect posture.

The sounds we choose to listen to—and the way we listen—can guide us towards a heightened awareness.

Dervishes performing ritual dance, Istanbul.

Silence

Ten thousand things are heard when born
But the highest heaven's always still.
Yet everything must begin in silence,
And into silence it vanishes.
—WEI YING-WU, EIGHTH-CENTURY CHINESE POET[7]

Each of us knows from our own experience that a "good listener" can change the mood, tenor, and even the level of conversation. And if by some act of grace, a moment of silence should materialize, then a truly precious opportunity is at hand.

Intentional silence is rare in the course of daily life. We tend to be uncomfortable with it, particularly in conversations, and rush in to fill the gap with anything—a thought, a joke, an association. Yet if by common consent this impulse is resisted and silence is respected and included in the fabric of conversation, then "mutual listening" can occur. This is the stuff of magic, of inspiration. It's our window, our psychic teleporter into the unknown.

From a moment of shared listening, a fresh line of thought, an insight invariably appears. You can witness this clearly when taping an interview. The best responses come in the pauses between questions, whenever the interviewer isn't so quick to jump in with his next query. The Japanese even have a name for this pause in conversation: they call it the *ma*. During business negotiations, the occasional *ma* is savored and appreciated. Needless to say, Westerners doing business with the Japanese for the first time tend to regard these pauses as a chance to interject another item from their agenda.

Many Quakers draw from moments of quiet to deepen religious experience, beginning their meetings with a collective silence from which individuals speak out when moved to do so. In such gatherings, it's often been observed that the speaker voices an idea that is occurring to many others in that instant—as if a current of thought was being collectively shared and individually expressed.

Physicist Ursula Franklin has said it is in such moments of programmed silence that "the unforeseen, unprogrammable events in our lives can occur."[8] Admittedly, in Western society such moments are rare. Yet it is by bringing more of them into the routine of our daily lives that the road to deeper listening lies.

According to audiologist Alfred Tomatis, the symbol of the question mark is derived from the shape of an ear. It is a clue, perhaps, that in the face of the unknown—the many challenges we humans face, and the decisions and opportunities that lie before us—the direction we need to move is toward listening.

Jim Metzner

SOUNDS OF HUMAN LIFE

WATER DRUMMING

There is music in all things, if men had ears. —LORD BYRON

The Mangbetu people make their home in northeastern Zaire, in a remote area that was not known to Westerners until 1870, when a party of European explorers arrived on the scene.

In this region of central Africa, tribal custom dictates that only men play musical instruments. While women may dance and sing the same songs as men, they're not permitted to play musical instruments. But the Mangbetu women have cleverly found a way around this prohibition by inventing new forms of music— ones that don't require conventional instruments. For example, they "play" large snail shells, rhythmically slapping their bodies with the shells' open end. Using different-sized shells, a group of women can create an incredible variety of percussive melodies.

Water Drumming features another form of grassroots percussion. When women gather at a river to do their washing, they often make music by using the surface of the river as a drum. Drumming with cupped hands and slaps of their forearms, they make a delightfully sloshy rhythm. To change pitch, the women simply vary the opening of their cupped hand.

Water drumming can serve as the rhythm section for both traditional and contemporary songs. The selections on your CD give an indication of some of the possible variations of rhythm and tone.

Although this form of music is casual and playful, the Mangbetu invest

OPPOSITE: MANGBETU WOMEN WATER DRUMMING, ZAIRE.

other categories of music with great significance. Traditional court music symbolizes and celebrates their king's authority while giving him the opportunity to showcase his dancing skill, which is regarded as a sign of intelligence and a highly desirable attribute for a ruler.[1]

A traditional Mangbetu court orchestra would include large wooden slit drums, skin-covered drums, ivory horns, trumpets, a double iron bell, whistles, and rattles. Such an ensemble performed for George Schweinfurth, one of the first Europeans to visit the Mangbetu in 1870: "(They) proceeded to execute solos upon their instruments. These men were advanced proficient in their art, and brought forth sounds of such power, compass, and flexibility that could be modulated from sounds like the roar of a hungry lion, or the trumpeting of an infuriated elephant, down to tones which might be compared to the sighing of the breeze or to a lover's whisper."[2]

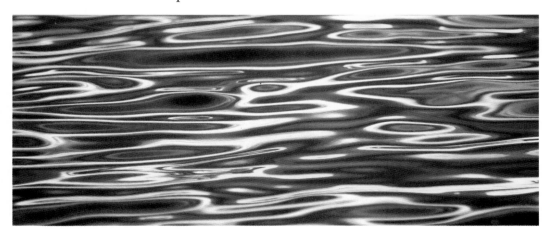

WATER SURFACE USED AS PERCUSSION BY THE MANGBETU.

BAYAKA SONG

A sound arises out of the earth—
a singing, a friendliness.
CEDRIC WRIGHT, FROM *EARTH PRAYERS*

Every Bayaka child is a musical prodigy. —LOUIS SARNO

Drawn by the beauty and mystery of pygmy music, American Louis Sarno traveled to the Central African Republic in 1986 to record the music firsthand and to steep himself in the culture that produced it. Since then, he has lived in the rain forest with a group of pygmies known as the Bayaka, or Ba-Benjellé.

Sarno's first contact was with a Bayaka settlement near a village, where the pygmies, like many of the world's indigenous peoples, have been lured part way into the "modern" world—living in squalid conditions on the fringes of roads, trading forest goods or their own labor for tobacco, cultivated crops, and Western products from local villagers.

After a time, though, Louis was permitted to accompany the Bayaka to their "other" world—the remote camps in the rain forest where they practice their traditional lifestyle of hunting and gathering. All the while, he was documenting the richness and complexity of their music.

"Music is in the air all the time, 24 hours a day," Sarno says. "At any given moment, a woman is singing a lullaby, someone else is playing a flute or a harp, or

children are sitting around humming. Each individual has a distinct musical personality, because they actually learn to sing before they can talk, just like they learn to dance before they can walk."[3]

Bayaka Song was recorded early in the morning, as a group of Bayaka women left their camp to gather *koko*, the edible leaf of a vine that grows deep in the forest. You can hear how beautifully the women's voices blend and resonate with the lush ambient sound of the forest. The Bayaka are keenly aware of the acoustical properties of their environment, according to Sarno, and their singing makes the best use of those characteristics.

"Bayaka music can be extremely complex," he says. "There are recognizable melodies, but they improvise around them. If someone makes a mistake, sings a wrong note, everyone notices and they usually laugh.

"When I first played back recordings to them, they were incredibly excited, laughing and giggling. They especially liked picking out their voices. Now they no longer laugh and giggle when they hear their music. They remind me of professional musicians listening carefully to their own performance. They know when the music is good and they know when it's not so inspired. I just find it endlessly fascinating."

Bayaka, Central African Republic.

KALULI SONG

The text of the song is considered a map that moves through places in the land. It names trees; it names specific places; it names waterfalls; it names birds that sing at those trees by those waterfalls. And by starting someplace far away and ending right where you are, or starting right where you are and ending up someplace far away, the song takes you on a journey. —STEVEN FELD, ETHNOMUSICOLOGIST

New Guinea, the second largest island in the world after Greenland, is home to a richly diverse group of cultures. It's estimated that at least 800 different languages are spoken there, among a total population of roughly three-and-a-half million people. Until recently, New Guinea was also one of the last places on earth where indigenous peoples lived in relative isolation from other societies.

To the Kaluli people of Papua New Guinea (the nation occupying the eastern half of the island), all sounds are voices in the forest: wind, water, rain, birds, insects, and even the songs of the Kaluli themselves, which are inspired by and sometimes mimic the sounds of nature. The Kaluli hear these voices as complex layers that overlap and interplay in continuously changing patterns. They even have a name for this, *dulugu ganalan*, which means "lift-up-over sounding."

Kaluli Song was recorded early in the morning against the background noise of the rain forest. In the distance you can hear the booming of the black jungle coucal, a prominent predawn bird of the rainy season. In the foreground you can hear a creek, one of many waterways that traverse Kaluli lands near

KALULI WOMEN SINGING AS THEY POUND SAGO, PAPUA NEW GUINEA.

Mt. Bosavi. Songs are often composed and sung near flowing water, which is a living metaphor for the flow of ideas that inspires the singer. In fact, the Kaluli say that composing a new song is like "having a waterfall in your head."

Soon you'll hear a number of women and children preparing *sago*, a staple of the local diet. The sago tree, a palm, has been split and its pulp is being scraped and pounded into a kind of cake. As she scrapes the sago pith with stone tools, a woman named Ulahi begins to sing, and her voice is echoed by her friend Eyobo. Ulahi sings to *ni babo*, her nephew, about searching for sago palms and finding them at a series of creeks. The song's lyrics outline a journey through the Kaluli landscape: *Deseb fele, Yesele, Sulu bese, Solo fele, Sowasiya*. This sequence of place names weaves a map in sound, leading to the very creek where Ulahi is pounding her sago.

The overlapping voices in song, another manifestation of "lift-up-over sounding," convey the feeling of loose, playful comradery so important to the Kaluli way of life. Ulahi's song finally fades into the sounds of late afternoon, as a chorus of butcherbirds blends with the hooting of a distant fruit dove.

Sadly, such moments may one day be a distant memory to the Kaluli. Deforestation is threatening Papua New Guinea's environment, and as people leave the rain forest, exposure to Western goods and a cash economy take a toll on their traditional culture. Kaluli ceremonial life is fast becoming an artifact, and few young people are composing songs or learning stories. This transformation underlines the importance of recordings such as this one, which can both document and reaffirm the value of indigenous cultures.

INITIATION RITE

Once a woman was chopping wood when a chip flew up and made a whirring noise as it passed her ear. She thought, "That sounds good." So she took pieces of wood and carved them until she found the right shape. Then she tied it to a string and made the first bullroarer. With it, she terrified people for a long time. She would come twirling the bullroarer and everybody would run away, afraid. One day a man stayed behind to see what was making this sound. He saw it was a woman, and he thought, "A voice this big should not be made by a woman." So he killed her and took the bullroarer. Ever since, the bullroarers have been the men's secret. —MALE CULT MYTH OF THE ILAHITA ARAPESH

The Ilahita Arapesh people are another of the multifarious cultures found in Papua New Guinea. They occupy seven villages and roam some 75 square miles in the northeastern part of the country.

The selection on your CD was recorded in May of 1986, in the village of Ilahita, located on the inland side of a coastal mountain range. What you hear is part of an elaborate initiation ritual for young boys between the ages of eight and fourteen. The men shouting are the fathers of boys being initiated, while that mysterious, low-frequency *whooshing* sound you hear is made by wooden noisemakers called "bullroarers," which play a key role in the ceremony.

Each bullroarer is made from a carved or flat piece of wood, similar in shape to a double-edged knife blade about seven or eight inches long. It's tied to the end of a long leather thong or rope and

BULLROARERS USED IN INITIATION RITUAL, PAPUA NEW GUINEA.

spun quickly around in circles to make the noise you hear. During the initiation rites, men from the village twirl the bullroarers fiercely in mock combat as the boys' fathers "attack" and eventually capture the bullroarers. Later they are presented to the boys (who passively witness the battle) as tokens of their initiation to this stage of manhood.

All their young lives, the Arapesh boys have heard the frightening noises of the bullroarer from afar, but have never seen their source. Until their initiation, they are told that the sounds are made by Lefin, a red-haired spirit dwarf who fashions wooden drums and slit-gongs by chewing them into shape.[4]

During the ritual you hear on the CD, the true nature of the noisemaker is finally revealed, and the boys are instructed in the proper technique of sounding the bullroarer. When twirled correctly, it becomes the deep, raspy voice of Lefin, saying over and over: "Ai tembi-tembineiii, Ai tembi-tembineiii," which in Arapesh means, "I am a great, great man."

This initiation to the secret of the bullroarer, though important, is just one of a series of mock-aggressive encounters that Arapesh men perform during the 40 or 50 years it takes to transmit all secrets from fathers to sons.

ARAPESH MAN DRESSED FOR INITIATION CEREMONY.

TIBETAN CHANT

The sound itself carries the insight.

—KONCHUK WANGDU, ABBOT OF THE GYUTÖ MONASTERY

One of the most remarkable forms of vocal music in the world comes from Tibet. It was virtually unknown to Westerners until 1964, when American cultural anthropologist Huston Smith visited the Buddhist monastery at Gyutö in northern India, and heard the monks there chanting during the observance of a tantric ritual.

I was on the verge of dozing off when I was brought to my senses abruptly by what sounded like an angelic choir. The monotone had given way to rich, full-chorded harmony. If the accompanying bells and cymbals had begun to simulate the tones of the King's Chapel organ, I would hardly have been more astonished. My first thought was: they're singing parts. This thought was striking enough, for I had always known harmony as a Western art form. But this jolt was nothing to the one that awaited me, for after several minutes of such chords the choir suddenly cut out, leaving everything to a single soloist or cantor. And he, seated perhaps ten feet to my right, was singing by himself what sounded like a three-tone major chord composed of a musical first, third, and faintly audible fifth.[5]

Listen carefully to *Tibetan Chant* and you'll hear that each member of the Gyutö choir is indeed singing several tones simultaneously. They do this by using special vocal techniques developed over the centuries.

ཕོཉ་ བསྐལ་པ་ཉི་མེ་ལྷུར་འབར་བཞི་རྟོང་
རྟུང་ནག་འཚོ་བ་དཀཔར་འཚོ་བ་པ་པོ

The human voice, whether sung or spoken, is composed of a fundamental tone and overtones. A voice singing middle C, for example, is a composite of tones that our brain identifies as a single sound. The monks of Gyütö have found a way to make certain overtones in their voices audible, by allowing them to resonate in the mouth, soft palate, and other parts of the upper body that support or dampen the vibrations produced by the vocal chords.

When the Gyütö monks intone their chant, it is part of an intense ritual activity. As they sing, their hands are continuously moving, as if they were also performing the chant in some silent, signed language. Their movements are subtle and precise. A novice monk may bring in a vase of holy water, and while the monks are chanting, gracefully moving their hands, turning the pages of text, the vase is passed down the line from monk to monk and presented as an offering.

In the midst of all this, the monks are also visualizing themselves as deities and meditating on the meaning of the chant's words, which are intentionally slurred so that even someone who speaks the Tibetan language could not under-stand them. Their esoteric meaning is for initiates only—those who have inten-

MUSICAL NOTATION FOR GYUTÖ MONK'S CHANT.

sively prepared and studied tantric Buddhism. Yet Konchuk Wangdu, abbot of the Gyutö monastery, acknowledges that the *sound* of the chant can have a beneficial effect, even for those who haven't studied Buddhism, and don't speak a word of Tibetan.[6]

Since the Chinese invasion and occupation of Tibet in the 1950s, the Gyutö monks have lived in exile in northern India. Their monastery is located in a restricted area, which makes it extremely difficult to attract novices. With the permission of the Dalai Lama, the monks have purchased land in neighboring Nepal and are building a new monastery and center for Buddhist studies.[7]

REINCARNATE LAMA, LUKLA MONASTERY.

SIBERIAN SHAMANS

My ayami *(spirit guide) gave me three assistants—the panther, the bear, and the tiger.*
Then she told me to make images of my assistant spirits and to wear them on my neck.
After they had been carved out as the ayami *prescribed, I hung them on the wall and*
brought them offerings and gave them food to eat and burned incense for them; then I
beat my drum, summoning the spirits to enter the images, and they obeyed my call.
—A SHAMAN OF THE TUNGUS PEOPLE, EASTERN SIBERIA, EARLY 20TH CENTURY

In many traditional cultures, man saw himself in a direct relationship with the forces of the natural and supernatural worlds. In Siberia the intermediaries between ordinary mortals and these forces were shamans, who were revered as healers, advisors, performers, arbiters of the inexplicable, and "tuners of the universe." Some were said to fly and perform other miraculous feats, such as being able to dismember and reassemble their bodies. Drumming and dancing, shamans performed ceremonies to heal and protect their neighbors, and to communicate with spirits.

"It was the drumming more than anything else that created the movement from the ordinary world to the world of spirits," says Thomas R. Miller, an anthropologist at the American Museum of Natural History. "The drum was considered the steed on which the shaman rode to the other world. Often, in fact, the shaman would actually place the drum between his legs as if it were a horse or reindeer and ride it to the other world. The patterns of drumming and singing opened a sonic window between this world and the others."

From 1897 to 1902, the Jesup Expedition of the American Museum of Natural History, one of the first and greatest anthropological expeditions, traveled throughout Siberia to trace cultural links between the native peoples of Siberia and the Pacific Northwest of the United States. Among the materials gathered

KORYAK SHAMAN WITH DRUM, SIBERIA.

were some of the earliest known recordings of shamans. These rare and fragile wax cylinders were preserved and recently transferred to tape.

The first selection on *Siberian Shamans* is a female shaman of the Koryak people (:41). It was recorded by Waldemar Jochelson in the Kamenskoye region of the Kamchatka Peninsula. The second selection is a male shaman of the Tungus people (1:27); it also was recorded by Jochelson, in the Kolyma region bordering the East Siberian Sea. Listen carefully and you'll hear the shaman mimicking animal sounds.

Tom Miller, who has studied these recordings, explains. "The shaman would travel to another world, make contact with a particular spirit—often an animal—and call it by name. This spirit would then enter his body and use his voice to communicate with humans.

"Typically, the shaman had a long chain attached to the back of his coat. His assistant would hold the other end of this chain while the shaman danced and drummed. This was so that the shaman was sure to come back to this world from the other world, because it was possible that he might get stuck there and not be able to return."

In the former Soviet Union, the rise of communism forced Siberian shamans underground in the early 1930s. However, with the dissolution of the USSR, there's been a resurgence of shamanic practices old and new, which coincides with a rekindled interest in traditional culture and identity. In the Sakha Republic, for example, rock groups are performing music derived from traditional shamanic songs and imagery.

NEPALESE CARAVAN

A bird note and the water rush command the stillness. Even in rain, this landscape is hallucinatory—gorges and waterfalls, the pines and clouds that come and go, fire-colored dwellings painted with odd flowers and bizarre designs, the cloud-mirrors of the rice paddies in steps down the steep mountainside, a flock of vermilion minivets, blown through a wind-tossed tumult of bamboo. —PETER MATTHIESSEN, *THE SNOW LEOPARD*

In the hills and mountains of Nepal, there are few roads. Instead, ancient footpaths traverse the landscape, hugging hillsides and following the pathways of rivers fed by the Himalayan watershed. Along these trails flow the people of Nepal and its visitors: Hindus and Buddhists on pilgrimages to holy sites, women carrying baskets of dried dung to use as fuel, farmers transporting large bundles of hay, children on their way to school, and a steady stream of trekkers from around the world who have to come to experience the extraordinary beauty of this country.

Caravans of yaks or donkeys also use the footpaths to transport goods throughout the hills of Nepal. Laden with baskets of produce and grain, salt and other necessities, these caravans thread their way along the narrow trails, accompanied by herders who sometimes sing and whistle to their animals. Bells are often hung around an animal's neck, some tied with a plain rope, others attached to colorfully embroidered harnesses.

On *Nepalese Caravan* you'll hear a chorus of bells announce the approach of a donkey caravan carrying goods from one Himalayan village to another. After

the several dozen animals have passed, the sound of the herdsman's whistle lingers as a haunting reminder.

This recording was made in 1982 on the trail around Annapurna, one of the more popular treks in Nepal. In a relatively short time, tourism (particularly trekking) has become an important source of revenue in this remote nation, which is also one of the world's poorest. Breathtaking scenery, friendly people, an ancient culture—these are the blessings of Nepal that attract multitudes from around the world.

Unfortunately, trekking has also contributed to one of Nepal's most serious ecological problems—deforestation. Over the past few decades, Nepal has seen much of its topsoil lost to erosion, and deforestation contributes greatly to the problem. Trekkers actually burn little firewood compared to most Nepalese. But in a well-traveled region even this limited use of wood can have a significant impact. Today visitors to Nepal are instructed to do as the caravans have done for generations—go lightly on the land.[8]

Caravan on mountain trail, Nepal.

THE ANIMAL KINGDOM

ANTS

One should pay attention to even the smallest crawling creature, for these too may have a valuable lesson to teach us, and even the smallest ant may wish to communicate with man. —BLACK ELK, SIOUX MEDICINE MAN

There are an estimated one to ten *million billion* ants crawling around on the earth's surface. Now a million billion ants weigh about a billion pounds—just slightly less than the combined weight of every man, woman, and child on earth. Which means that the total number of ants outweighs us ten to one. So what's the secret of this insect's success?

"Ants have evolved the most successful societies in the invertebrate world, with complex caste systems and…the most advanced system of chemical communication in the animal kingdom," says noted entomologist E. O. Wilson of Harvard University. "This has enabled them to be one of the most abundant and influential organisms on earth for more than 60 million years."

From the planet's point of view, ants are a lot more useful than we are. As scavengers, composters, pollinators, and predators of insects and small animals, ants are essential; their loss would be catastrophic to virtually every ecosystem. They are indeed, as Professor Wilson has noted, the little things that run the earth.[9]

This recording was made by placing a small lavaliere microphone (the kind you sometimes see pinned to the lapels of TV announcers) inside the entrance of an anthill. What you're hearing are the "stridulations" of red ants, *Pogonomyrmex*

maricopa, recorded in Arizona's Sonoran Desert. The ants produce these squeaking sounds by rubbing two parts of their body together, usually waist against abdomen.

Ants communicate primarily through chemical exchanges with their neighbors, so these stridulations may have a specialized purpose. Some ants stridulate when they find food, but mainly, entomologists think, they make the sounds when in distress—such as when some two-legged behemoth places a giant listening device on their doorstep.

LEAFCUTTER ANTS, PANAMA.

LEAFHOPPERS

The speech of insects
  and the speech of men
    are heard
with different ears.
—SHIKI, LATE 19TH-CENTURY JAPANESE POET

I doubt that anyone hearing these strange noises for the first time would guess that they were listening to a tiny insect called a leafhopper, which lives on vegetation of all kinds, especially grasses. The sounds you hear were recorded in an unusual way: a phonograph stylus was placed against the stem of a plant on which a leafhopper was resting. The stylus picked up the insect's vibrations and translated them into electrical impulses, which were then fed into a preamplifier and tape recorder.

Scientists speculate that what you're hearing is the leafhopper's courtship song, which it uses to attract members of the opposite sex. These vibrations would travel only a half inch through the open air, but have a much larger range—three to five feet—when transmitted through the plants on which the leafhoppers live and feed. That may not sound very far, but given the number of leafhoppers that crowd each plant, four to five feet is plenty. A more powerful signal would risk revealing their location to predators.

When an insect senses (through the layer of tiny hairs covering its body) the vibratory call of a prospective mate, it responds with its own call. Characteris-

OPPOSITE: RED-BANDED LEAFHOPPERS, ILLINOIS.

tically, the male stays where he is while producing a relatively complex song. The female moves towards him over the plant's surface. Her response is much simpler than the male's song, and sounds to our ears like cooing.

On your recording, the first sound you hear is the courtship song of a male *Eupteryx cyclops* leafhopper, which lasts for 28 seconds. At the (:05) and (:18) marks, you can hear the "cooing" response of the female leafhopper. Next you hear a courtship song (:20) of a closely related species of leafhopper, *E. urticae*; with a female reply at the (:03), (:10), and (:17) intervals. Although these two species of leafhoppers are nearly identical, their songs are quite different, as you can hear. Finally you hear a "duet" (:42) between the male and female of a third species, *E. aurata.* Here the male's rhythmic song is decidedly longer. The female coos in reply at (:14) and (:29).

Leafhoppers are one of the most notorious transmitters of plant viruses on earth, and certain species are responsible for major crop damage. A hungry host of brown planthoppers can flatten a Philippine rice field as thoroughly as a stamped-ing herd of cattle.[10] Unfortunately, most leafhoppers look alike, and it's hard to control insect pests when you can't correctly identify the culprits.

Experts now believe that the distinctive sound of each species is the key by which identification, and control, might be possible. One approach would be to lure the insects into a trap with recordings of their mating calls. These would be transmitted not through the air, but leafhopper-style—conductively, through the plants they live on.

TERMITES

The rapidity with which (African termites) work is remarkable, and in a single night they have been known to burrow up through the leg of a table, then across the table, stopping on the way to devour the articles lying on it, and down through another leg into the floor again. —RICHARD LYDEKKER, NATURALIST

To a homeowner, the word "termite" calls forth a number of associations, none of them good: rotted timbers, exterminators, expense, plunging property values. But take humans (and our possessions) out of the picture for a moment and a new appreciation of termites emerges.

By eating the cellulose in dead wood, they help decompose fallen trees and stumps, recycling wood debris into soil. Like ants, termites display a highly adaptive, mutually cooperative, complex social organization in their colonies, whose populations number in the millions.[11]

Many species of termites make their home in fallen trees or timber, hollowing out galleries as they munch their way through the wood. Some African species build nest mounds of clay up to 14 feet tall, laced with a network of tunnels extending dozens of feet underground. The colony heard on *Termites* is enjoying a late-night meal in the Central African Republic.

Mound-dwelling termites are often eaten as a delicacy in Africa and other tropical areas. The Baka people of Cameroon usually wait until the beginning of the rainy season, when the termites are most likely to be living in the upper levels of the mound. They then blow smoke into the subterranean passages, which forces the termites toward the tip of the mound and keeps them from retreating underground. At that point, the mound is broken open and the termites are harvested and eaten.

CLAY TERMITE MOUND, BOTSWANA.

BATS

All night, in happiness, she hunts and flies.
Her high sharp cries
Like shining needlepoints of sound
Go out into the night, and echoing back,
Tell her what they have touched.
—RANDALL JARRELL, FROM HIS POEM "BATS"

Neither bird nor mouse, the bat is the only winged, flying mammal. Many species, including the moustache bats that appear on your recording, use high-frequency signals to navigate their environment— a technique called *echolocation.*

In its larnyx the bat produces short ultrasonic pulses that bounce off nearby objects and return to the bat as echoes. These returning echoes are analyzed almost instantaneously, and help the bat orient itself in dark places, as well as to locate and capture flying prey. Some bats are even able to echolocate and eat at the same time by transmitting signals through their nostils!

Whether transmitted from the bat's nose or mouth, these echolocation signals are well above the range of human hearing.[12] To make the recording on your CD, we used a device called a "bat detector" to translate the bat's high frequencies to sounds within our audible range. You can hear how noisy a colony of about 20 bats can be. Now imagine tuning in a bat cave where *thousands* of bats are echolocating simultaneously!

Amazingly, bats seem able to pick out the sound of their own echo amidst the cacophony of their fellow cave-dwellers. Scientists don't know precisely how bats do it, but they suspect it's a highly refined version of the "Cocktail Party Effect" in humans (see page 13), which enables our ear and brain to tune out background noise and concentrate on one sound.

Bats may be the acknowledged masters of echolocation, but they're not the only creatures with a built-in sonar system. Certain species of birds, rats, and dolphins also echolocate. Even humans share this ability, to a limited extent. Whenever a blind person taps his cane, he is listening for the returning echoes of sound to detect nearby objects. Anyone who can hear knows intuitively, by sound alone, whether or not they are in an enclosed space or outdoors. It's the returning echoes of sound that give us the "sense" of being indoors.

In Western societies the bat has acquired a bad reputation, but the reasons are based more on hearsay than scientific fact. In China, on the other hand, bats have been revered as symbols of good luck for centuries. By all accounts, we owe these tireless predators a debt of gratitude. All over the world, bats are vital players in virtually every ecosystem, dispersing seeds and pollinating flowering plants.[13] Who's to say what this world would be like if bats lost their appetite for night-flying insect pests? It's been estimated that a single colony in Texas (composed of 20 million bats) eats half a million pounds of insects each night.

OPPOSITE: EMERGING MEXICAN FREE-TAILED BATS, BRACKEN CAVE, TEXAS. ABOVE: RED BATS IN FLIGHT.

BIRD SONG

You listen now to this thrush's song, deliberate and almost serene. The phrases are clear, precise and with casual pauses between them. There is no rush about this singing, nor even any sense of effort. It is like a breeze in the woods, like the flow of a brook. Ay-oleee. *And after a pause,* Olee-ay. *Not exultant, as the singing of an oriole, nor effusive as the wrens, but announcing that life itself deserves a song. You listen and your pulse begins to slacken. The thrush still sings.* —HAL BORLAND, *TWELVE MOONS OF THE YEAR*

A familiar character in fairytales and myth is the hero who overcomes a great challenge, and is rewarded with the power to understand the language of birds.[14] As veteran eavesdroppers and astute observers of the human scene, the birds invariably offer the hero savvy advice.

For most mortals, there's no denying the pleasure that bird calls bring. If we slow down recordings of birds like the thrushes featured on *Bird Song*, a hidden realm of complexity and beauty is revealed. Personally, I hear echoes of a primeval music, familiar yet exotic, like Eastern tones put to a Western rhythm.

The song of the wood thrush, for example, is really three phrases in succession. It begins with a series of pure, whistled tones (thought to communicate long distances), followed by a more melodic phrase; it ends with a rapid trill of notes. The sonogram on page 54 is a sound-picture of this thrush's song. As in musical notation, each note is represented by a mark on the grid, which is read horizontally from left to right. The higher the frequency, the higher the mark appears on the grid. The density of each mark corresponds to the intensity of the sound it denotes.

Veery, Ontario, Canada.

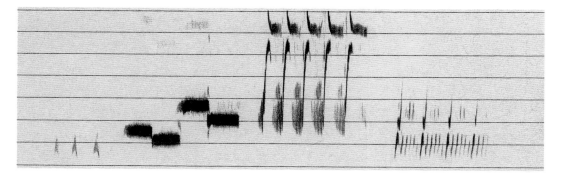

On *Bird Song* you'll hear a sampling of song from a variety of thrushes in this order: wood thrush (:40), veery (:40), hermit thrush (:30), gray-cheeked thrush (:41), and Swainson's thrush (:29). You'll hear each bird's song twice—once at normal speed and a second time at one-quarter speed.

Today the mysteries of bird song are luring animal behaviorists as never before. Although scientists question whether bird song is truly a language, most agree that it is a complex trait that requires that a bird learn from other members of its species.[15] Like language, bird song carries information, even dialect. A local flock may have its own version of its species' song, as distinct from another dialect of the same species as a southern drawl is from Brooklynese.

Animal behaviorists also suggest that the parts of a bird's song are suited for different purposes. Loud, sustained, pure tones may be declarations of territoriality to the avian world at large, while quieter, more complex passages could contain a more intimate message for nearby family members. Of course, there's always the possibility—my favorite theory—that birds also sing for the sheer joy of it.

SONOGRAM OF WOOD THRUSH'S SONG.

ELEPHANTS

The elephant moves slowly to protect its vast brain,
With which it hears subsonic sound,
And in which it carries the topology,
The resonances and reverberations,
Of a continent.

—HEATHCOTE WILLIAMS, "SACRED ELEPHANT"

One of the great mysteries of elephant behavior is how males find females at mating time. It's a daunting challenge, since female elephants are sexually receptive, on average, only one day a year. To make matters worse, adult males live apart from female groups, often by as much as several miles.

Still, generations of elephants prove that males do indeed get to the right place at the right time. Their keen sense of smell probably helps, but smell alone can't account for the elephant's success in all conditions, given the distances involved.

Here's another mystery: how could groups of elephants, separated by several miles, move together in a coordinated fashion as if being choreographed by an unseen director? Groups of radio-collared elephants have been observed doing just that—moving along parallel lines, turning in unison, and converging from distant points—even when wind conditions prevented the transmission of odor from one group to another.

The answers seem to lie in the world of sound. A number of researchers have studied speeded-up recordings of elephant vocalizations and discovered there is a component in the elephant's voice that is *infrasonic*, or below the range of human hearing.[16] Whales are thought to use such low-frequency sounds to communicate with each other over vast tracts of ocean. Elephants may have the same ability, sending their long-distance calls through the air instead of water.

Acoustically, low-frequency signals can be heard over greater distances than high-frequency signals—which is why you can hear thunderstorms rumble from many miles away. To test the range of low-frequency elephant vocalizations, researchers in Etosha National Park in Namibia played recordings of menstruating females over an outdoor loudspeaker. The responses of distant males showed that they could hear the calls from at least two-and-a-half miles away.

On your recording, you'll first hear elephant calls at normal speed— just on the edge of what most humans can detect in the low-frequency range. Then you'll hear the same vocalizations at three times normal speed, which places the low-frequency sounds well within the range of our hearing. The first selection was recorded at Amboseli National Park in Kenya. It captures the voice of Zita, a young female elephant, as she makes six post-copulatory calls [(:35) normal speed, (:11) 3x]. The second recording was made at night in Etosha National Park, where a group of elephants at a waterhole communicate with rumbles and screams [(:35) normal speed, (:11) 3x].

ELEPHANTS AND EGRETS, UGANDA.

BEARDED SEALS

O sea goddess Nuliajuk, / when you were a little unwanted orphan girl
we let you drown. / You fell in the water
and when you hung onto the kayaks crying / we cut off your fingers.
So you sank into the sea / and your fingers turned into
the innumerable seals.

You dear little orphan, / creep out of the water
panting on this beautiful shore, / puh, puh, like this, puh, puh,
O welcome gift / in the shape of a seal!
—NETSILIK ESKIMO PRAYER

The first humans to hear the eerie vocalizations of the bearded seal, *Erignathus barbatus*, were probably Eskimos with their ears pressed against the hulls of their wooden boats. Hunters would listen for a certain note in the seal's song (a moan, following the pause after the descending warble) that indicated the seal, a mammal, was about to surface and breathe. [17]

The bearded seals on this CD were recorded with a hydrophone, or underwater microphone, beneath the Arctic ice off Pt. Barrow, Alaska, in the spring of 1980. The ice in this part of the Arctic Ocean ranges in thickness from several inches to 20 or 30 feet. There are many cracks and fissures in the ice that the seals breathe through during winter, maintaining a network of holes kept open by constant use.

BEARDED SEAL, ELLESMERE ISLAND.

Occasionally the seals will emerge and bask in the sun on the frozen "roof" of their world. Since bearded seals live most of their lives under the ice, very little is known about their behavior. This makes their vocalizations especially valuable in locating the animals as they swim in the frigid waters. Choruses of bearded seals have been heard with a hydrophone, from distances of up to 20 miles.

The size of the group you hear in this recording is unknown, but may number in the hundreds; seals are social animals and often congregate around breathing holes. From time to time in this recording you'll also hear a low-pitched grunt or two—the vocalizations of bowhead whales.

The development of multichannel recordings has enabled scientists to track the movements of individual seals—and brought them closer to answering such questions as: does a seal have a signature to its song that identifies it as an individual? (They may all sound alike to us, but imagine a seal trying to distinguish between human singing voices.) Do individuals or small groups of animals stay within the strict boundaries of a territory, or do large numbers of seals simply move around in a general area? These are all questions that time—and careful listening—may answer.

COYOTES

Long ago when the world was dark, the Creator told all the animals to gather shiny stones and throw them carefully into the sky, making pictures of themselves. The animals obeyed, and soon star-pictures—the constellations—hung in the sky. But not all were strong enough to throw their stones into the sky. So the Creator gave Coyote a whole sack of shiny stones and ordered him to make star portraits of the smaller animals. Coyote growled in dismay. Then, disobeying the Creator, he opened the sack and with one mighty heave tossed the entire jumble of shining stones into the heavens and made the Milky Way. Coyote laughed at the mischief he'd made, but his laughter soon turned to a cry of anguish: in his haste he'd neglected to make a picture of himself—the great trickster. Since then, whenever he looks at the night sky, Coyote barks and howls in dismay.
—HOPI STORY

In many Native American traditions, Old Man Coyote is the archetypal trickster—seducing, cajoling, and swindling his way through epic misadventures. He is generally up to no good, although more often than not the tables turn on him. Then Old Man Coyote is humbled, if only for the moment.

Real-life coyotes *(Canis latrans)* have acquired their own measure of notoriety, mostly for their habit of preying on domestic livestock. Originally found only in western North America, in the last half-century coyotes have expanded their range to the northeastern United States, apparently filling the predators' niche left vacant by the wolf, an endangered species that's been systematically wiped out in most regions of the country. In the Northeast, the coyote is

one of the few animals besides man that prey upon deer, helping to check the growth of an animal that has become too populous for its available habitat. Coyotes also help control rodent populations.

The chorus on *Coyotes* was recorded after sundown in Organ Pipe Cactus National Monument near the Arizona-Mexico border.

Animal behaviorists have analyzed coyote vocalizations and divided them into a number of categories, including growls, huffs, woofs, barks, bark-howls, whines, wow-oo-wows, yelps, lone howls, group howls, and group yip-howls. Each of these has been linked to a different type of behavior. The growl, for example, is said to be used primarily as an all-purpose, low-grade threat. The group yip-howl is thought to declare and defend territory. Barks and woofs can apparently serve as either threat display or alarm call.[18]

On the other hand, some researchers question whether the behavior of coyotes or any animal can be categorically linked to a particular vocalization. They point out that animals, like humans, may use the same sound for different purposes, depending upon the circumstances.

Coyotes are nothing if not flexible: they hunt individually or in packs, depending on the nature and abundance of their prey. They're positively uncanny in their ability to disappear into their environment, which has served them well in their recent move from the prairies to the outskirts of town. This kind of adaptability has enabled Old Man Coyote to survive and flourish in a changing world, even as other wild predators vanish from the scene.

Opposite: Howling coyote, Montana.

COLOBUS MONKEYS

When the Monkey King was dying, he sent for his three sons. The first to arrive was Tebe, the redtail, who was made king of the forest. The next to come was Bururu, the colobus, who was made prime minister and given long black-and-white fur for his robes of office. The third son arrived long after. This was Nyani, the baboon, who was doomed to be the lowliest of monkeys. —EAST AFRICAN MYTH

Kenya's Kakamega forest lies just north of Lake Victoria and west of the country's highland region. It's a patchwork affair, crisscrossed by a network of roads, villages, and small farms.

In the early pre-dawn hours, a thick, cool blanket of moisture envelopes the forest. In the darkness the trees themselves seem to hiss. Dew drops roll off their leaves, producing a continuous, percussive patter. The humid air and the moist ground cover seem to magnify any noise, and the early riser is in touch with the hidden forest only through its sounds.

Then, faintly through the mist, the distant voices of a few black and white colobus monkeys *(Colobus guereza)* echo through the Kakamega. Each evening these monkeys sleep in "dormitory" trees, often quite far from one another. As dawn approaches, the troop begins to reestablish contact by calling into the jungle. Later they will regroup to search for food.

On your recording you can hear this chorus of monkeys build to a crescendo and reverberate through the forest. Then after a moment's pause, an individual monkey nearby begins the cycle anew.

When colobus monkeys were first observed, zoologists noticed that their hands lacked thumbs. Some theorized that the thumbs had been cut off; hence the name *colobus,* meaning "the mutilated one."

Before World War I, monkey furs were considered the height of fashion in Europe. Colobus monkeys were particularly sought after because of their beauty, and in some areas the species was nearly wiped out. Since then, of course, styles have changed—and the colobus has rebounded accordingly.[19]

Colobus monkey, Lake Naivasha, Kenya.

GIBBONS

Chiao-chiao sing the gibbons in the night,
Heavy are the mists gathering in the morning.
I do not know whether their calls are near or far,
For I only see mountain rising after mountain.
The gibbons love to sing on the eastern range,
Waiting for the answer from those on the western cliff.
—SHÊN YÜEH, FIFTH-CENTURY CHINESE POET

Gibbons, the acrobats of the ape world, comprise the family *Hylobatidae*, which means "tree traverser." They spend most of their lives swinging through the upper canopies of the tropical rainforests of Southeast Asia. While brachiating among these islands in the sky, gibbons often make leaps of 30 feet from tree to tree. They are also remarkable in their social system: most species of gibbons are both monogamous and territorial—traits rarely found together in mammals.

In the predawn hours, the singing performances of gibbons dominate the soundscape of the rain forest. About an hour before sunrise, male gibbons start by singing short, simple songs. Gradually the songs become longer and more elaborate, as if each male gibbon were trying to outperform his neighbors. Scientists hypothesize that these singing "competitions" play a role in the defense of territory.

After the males' singing, mated pairs of gibbons begin to vocalize duets.

Then the female delivers the most dramatic moment of all—the "great call"—as she swings rapidly through the treetops while her male partner follows in silence. The female often plays an agressive role in defending the mated pair's territory, and her performances of the great call and the duet appear to work together with the male's call to stake out the family turf.

The first selection (:42) is the morning song of a male agile gibbon, *Hylobates agilis*, recorded in the rain forest of Borneo. In the second selection (1:55), you'll hear a chorus of two females, perhaps a mother and daughter, work their way up to the crescendo of the great call. At the end of the call, there's a coda where the male's voice joins in briefly, and the cycle starts again.

Bornean gibbon, Sabah, Borneo.

OROPENDOLA BIRD

"… the sounds of multifarious life came from the vegetation around. The whirring of cicadas; the shrill stridulation of a vast number and variety of field crickets and grass-hoppers, each species sounding its peculiar note; the plaintive hooting of tree frogs—all blended together in one continuous ringing sound, the audible expression of the teeming profusion of Nature. …This uproar of life, I afterwards found, never wholly ceased, night or day: in course of time I became, like other residents, accustomed to it."
—HENRY WALTER BATES, 1848, NATURALIST AND EARLY EXPLORER OF THE AMAZON

Imagine yourself in the heart of the Brazilian Amazon, about 25 arduous miles from the main road linking Manaus, Brazil, to Venezuela. It is here in the wilderness that Thomas Lovejoy of the Smithsonian Institution established a research site to pioneer the study of rain-forest fragmentation.

It's late in the afternoon and the typical "wash" of rain forest sound is interrupted by the occasional roar of distant thunder, heralding the approach of a daily afternoon downpour. Suddenly the humid air is filled with a sound so bizarre that it seems completely out of place here—as if some Rube Goldbergesque mechanical contraption has materialized in the Amazon basin, pouring milk from a bottle, feeding coins into a slot machine, and finally hitting the jackpot.

Perched in the canopy 75 feet overhead is the source of all this racket—the male green oropendola bird, *Psarocolius viridis,* a relative of the oriole and the American blackbird, whose ear-bending territorial call may be worth a trip to South America all by itself.

The oropendola makes this extraordinary sound while hanging upside down from a tree branch, suspended like an ornament. The snapping you hear at (:32) on your recording following the glissando is probably the sound of a quick wing flap the bird uses to return to an upright perch.

Equipped with such a voice, a dominant male oropendola may service a whole colony of nests and a sizeable "harem" of females. Typically a host of opportunistic second-string males will be nearby, waiting for the dominant male to leave or show signs of weakness. His striking call is thought to keep his rivals at bay—while simultaneously advertising for mates.

Like many residents of the world's rain forests, oropendolas both green and russet-backed are severely threatened by what botanists like Thomas Lovejoy call "fragmentation"—the carving up of vast expanses of rain forest into smaller patches by loggers, farmers, and roadbuilders. Such activity has a drastic effect on the interdependent community of rain forest plants and animals, often resulting in a massive loss of species.

RUSSET-BACKED OROPENDOLA BIRD, VENEZUELA.

JAPANESE DEER

Twelve hundred years ago, Nara on the island of Honshu was the capital of Japan and its cultural center. Today, Nara's magnificent temples, shrines, and artistic treasures are a vivid reminder of its historic past.

One of Japan's most famous Shinto shrines is situated in Nara Park near the city's center. Founded in 768 by the Fujiwara clan, the Kasuga Shrine was originally dedicated to four deities. Deer were thought to be special messengers sent by the first Kasuga deity, and since ancient times the deer that roam Nara Park have been considered sacred. Revered and protected, a herd of about a thousand deer has become quite tame, strolling without concern among the park's many tourists.

The *Japanese Deer* were recorded in October during their rutting season, when their peculiar calls echo through the forest and lawns of Nara Park. Elsewhere in Japan the deer population has not fared nearly so well, although deer were once found in abundance throughout the country, particularly on Hokkaido, Japan's northernmost island.

Women and sacred deer, Mikasayama.

NATURE TRANSFORMED

SHISHI ODOSHI

Long ago the Japanese developed a clever device to shoo deer away from their gardens. The *shishi odoshi* (deer-scarer) is a bamboo pipe balanced on a fulcrum like a seesaw, with one end of the pipe hollowed out to form a cup. The device is placed in a stream, with the hollow end positioned to catch the flow of falling water from another pipe or a small waterfall.

As the shishi odoshi fills with water its balance shifts, causing the heavier end (now filled with water) to drop. As it does, the water drains back out, again shifting the weight and causing the other end to drop. It's this second drop, usually against a flat stone, that gives the shishi odoshi its characteristic sound, which chases deer away.

Nowadays shishi odoshi are as scarce as deer, preserved mainly as a curiosity in some temple gardens. The sound on your CD was recorded at Shisendo Temple in Kyoto.

SHISHI ODOSHI, *GARDEN OF RYOANJI.*

SUIKINKUTSU

Ears of my old age,
The summer rains
Falling down the rain-pipe.
—BUSON (1716-1783)

Imagine a world where every manmade object, no matter how simple, was designed to please the senses as well as perform its job—a place where form melded with function in the service of a high aesthetic. Japan has traditionally been such a world; it was there that the *suikinkutsu* (soo-ee KEEN-koots) was born—a clay cistern that was designed to also produce pleasing sounds.

Historically the suikinkutsu's place was in the rural Japanese garden next to the *tskubai* (skoo-bye), a large stone basin filled with water. Whenever a visitor would dip a wooden ladle into the tskubai to drink or wash, the overflow would drain onto a small circle of smooth rocks on the ground. Beneath these rocks was the suikinkutsu, which means literally "water-harp-cave." Consisting of a large, inverted, flat-bottomed clay pot, it was designed to provide drainage while producing beautiful sounds.

No one knows for sure when the suikinkutsu was invented; in fact, their existence was all but forgotten until the early 1980s, when a Japanese newspaper article described the discovery of this curious device in the garden of a Tokyo home. Since then dozens more have been either discovered or newly constructed throughout Japan.

CROSS SECTION OF SUIKINKUTSU.

In a Japanese garden, the sound you hear so clearly on your CD would be somewhat masked by the outdoor ambience. So listening to the sound—enjoying it—would require a pause in the normal routine of the day. One would have to take a moment and wait for the water to drip into the cavity below, perhaps even kneeling to hear the subtle nuances of sound.

These days the ambient noise level of Japanese cities and most suburbs is so high that some owners of outdoor suikinkutsus use bamboo pipes to amplify the sound: one end is placed near the mouth of the suikinkutsu, the other is held to the ear, stethoscope-style.

TSKUBAI, *GARDEN OF SANZEN-IN, KYOTO.*

AEOLIAN HARP

You, instrument mysterious
Of a muse born of the air,
Begin,
And again begin
Your melodious lament.

—EDUARD MORÏKE, "TO AN AEOLIAN HARP"

The world has always marveled at the beauty of wind-borne sound: ancient Greek legends tell of how Hermes invented the lyre after hearing the wind blow through the dried sinews of a turtle's carcass. King David's harp was said to hum when a nocturnal breeze played over its strings. And for centuries the Chinese have flown kites with taut strings made to sing in the wind.

Yet the phenomenon of wind-generated tones was still couched in mystery when German mathematician Athansius Kircher built the first-known Western wind harp in 1652. During the 18th and 19th centuries the Aeolian harp (named for Aeolus, the Greek god of winds) became fashionable in England and Germany, where its sounds could often be heard wafting from aristocrats' gardens, rooftops, and windowsills.

The Aeolian harp is aptly named, since its ethereal tones can be made by the wind alone as it plays over the strings. The instrument in your recording has 12 strings of varying thickness tuned in unison. It was placed flat in a window on

AEOLIAN HARPS.

a windy day, with the sash lowered to a height of about one inch above the strings. A good stiff breeze produced the sustained tones you hear.

The harp's distinctive sound is created by the resonance between two vibrations—one in the strings, the other in the currents of wind that blow over them. The strings vibrate slightly from the wind, but this in itself isn't audible. What can be heard is the result of another effect of the wind, which produces eddy currents of air behind each vibrating string, just as a flowing stream of water forms eddies behind a boulder. The higher the velocity of wind and the narrower the gauge of string, the more eddy currents are produced. When the frequency (the number of vibrations per second) of the eddy matches the fundamental frequency of the vibrating string or any of its harmonics, then we hear the song of the harp.

Music composer holding aeolian harp to the wind, Fairbanks, Alaska.

SOUNDS OF THE EARTH

TORNADO

I saw that the lower end, which had been sweeping the ground, was beginning to rise. I knew what that meant, so I kept my position. At last the great shaggy end of the funnel hung directly overhead. Everything was as still as death. There was a strong gassy odor and it seemed that I could not breathe. There was a screaming, hissing sound coming directly from the end of the funnel. I looked up and to my astonishment I saw right up into the heart of the tornado. There was a circular opening in the center of the funnel, about 50 or 100 feet in diameter, and extending straight upward at least one half-mile. The walls of this opening were of rotating clouds and the whole was made brilliantly visible by constant flashes of lightning which zigzagged from side to side.
—WITNESS TO A TORNADO, GREENSBURG, KANSAS, 1928

One of the worst storms in memory roared across the southern United States on April 3, 1974, spawning tornadoes by the dozens as it swept warm air against cold. One of these tornadoes struck without warning just outside Guin, Alabama, where it left a wake of destruction 138 miles long and claimed 26 lives.

As part of a Boy Scout project, Richard Alan Lindley of Guin was hoping to tape-record a severe weather warning on the radio. As the tornado approached, Richard put his tape recorder near a window and left it on while he ran across the street to warn his neighbors. Then he raced back to his own house to take cover.

The excerpt from Richard's recording begins a moment before the funnel cloud arrives. First you will hear the incredible force of the winds, followed by a

OPPOSITE: TORNADO OF JULY 16, 1979, CHEYENNE, WYOMING.

change in the tornado's pitch as the house's windows shatter. Richard and his family survived the twister, by the way, although their home was damaged. Another family in their neighborhood perished in the storm.

Recordings of tornadoes are rare indeed. The Guin tape, one of the most complete recordings to date, is a treasure for scientists studying the wind speed and energy of tornadoes, which are produced by intense storm systems when a mass of warm, moist air collides with cold, dry air and a rotation pattern begins.[20]

Only about one thunderstorm in a thousand will cause a tornado. In most storms, the rising warm air is blocked when it encounters a cooler layer. But in a severe thunderstorm, rising and falling airstreams can actually feed each other, helping to create a vortex with an incredibly powerful updraft.

Other storm systems, such as hurricanes, can be active for days, but conditions suitable for producing a tornado usually last just a few minutes. With wind speeds of up to 300 miles an hour, they are one of nature's most devastating and unpredictable forces. And this much is certain: no one who has ever seen a funnel cloud approaching will ever forget the sight—or the sound—of a writhing, gray-black sky-serpent bent on destruction.

EARTHQUAKE

… all the shrubs and trees began to move from their very roots, the ground rose and fell in successive furrows like the ruffled waters of a lake, and I became bewildered in my ideas, as I too plainly discovered that all this awful commotion in nature was the result of an earthquake. —JAMES AUDUBON, JOURNAL, NOVEMBER 1812

As any seismologist can tell you, the surface of our planet is in continuous motion. This movement is usually too subtle for us to feel, although scientists equipped with geophones (underground microphones) can monitor faint seismic activity as a very low frequency vibration. The shock of an earthquake disrupts this "background hum."

Earthquake was recorded during a 1985 quake centered off the coast of Wales. The loud sound you hear is the earthquake itself, followed by a series of aftershocks. You'll hear it first speeded up 40 times (:11), then 20 times (:22).

Scientists discovered in the late 1960s that the earth's crust is made up of tectonic plates, which on a planetary scale resemble pieces of a huge jigsaw puzzle. These plates move in relation to each other (usually about three-quarters of an inch per year), and are themselves subject to dynamic forces such as earth's gravity, the gravitational pull of the moon, and the movement of hot rock in the upper layers of the mantle.

For seismologists, any deviation from the typical "background noise" of the rock they're listening to could be a clue that some form of disturbance, and possibly an earthquake, is imminent. Many quakes occur along the "jigsaw lines" where the earth's tectonic plates meet. As these plates rub against or override each other, they often bind in place, accumulating a tremendous amount of force before slipping free. The shock waves from this slippage is what we surface-dwellers experience as an earthquake.

EARTHQUAKE REGISTERING 7.3 ON RICHTER SCALE, FUKUI, JAPAN.

LAVA FLOW

This sound was recorded in Hawaii on the slopes of Mount Kilauea, one of the world's most active volcanoes and the legendary dwelling place of Pe-le, the Hawaiian goddess of volcanic fire. Since 1983 Kilauea has been in almost continuous eruption, which makes it an idea "window" on the earth's interior—and a great place to study the dynamics of volcanic eruption.

Volcanoes are often categorized by the violence of their eruptions. Compared to explosive volcanoes like Mount Pinatubo or Mount St. Helens, Hawaiian volcanoes are relatively mild- mannered; they usually erupt in fluid lava flows instead of gaseous cataclysms.

These lava flows are divided into two main types: aa (pronounced "aH-ah"), and pahoehoe ("pa-HOI-hoi"). Pahoehoe moves rapidly, like a river of water. The type heard on *Lava Flow*, aa, is much slower—so slow, in fact, that the lava bulges and folds over itself as it flows along the ground.

The sound you hear on the CD is the surface crust falling off the front and sides of the aa flow. Like glass, this kind of lava (basaltic magma) is a silicate

Lava meets Pacific Ocean, Hawaii Volcanoes National Park.

liquid, which is why it sounds like something from the back end of a garbage truck. As the lava cools quickly and breaks, it forms a brittle glass.

This recording was made during a 1983 eruption of Kilauea, when the aa flow was moving at a rate of about 12 inches per minute. That is a fairly typical aa pace, according to scientists at the Hawaiian Volcano Observatory, which is perched on the rim of Kilauea's caldera (the bowl-shaped depression at the summit). Founded in 1912 by Thomas A. Jaggar, the observatory is operated by the U.S. Geological Survey and serves as a training ground for volcanologists from around the world.

VOLCANIC ERUPTION IN VARUNGA MOUNTAINS, ZAIRE.

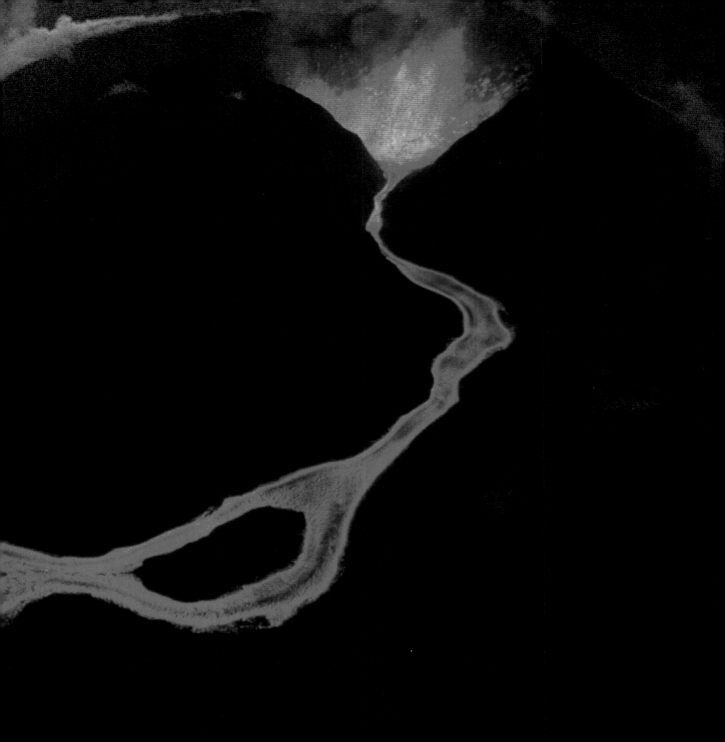

BOOMING SANDS

It is customary on the tuan-wu *day (a Dragon festival held on the fifth day of the fifth moon) for men and women from the city to clamber up to some of the highest points and rush down again in a body, which causes the sand to give forth a loud rumbling sound like thunder. Yet when you come to look at it the next morning, the hill is found to be just as steep as before. The ancients called this hill the Sounding Sand; they deified the sand and worshiped it there.* —TUN HUANG LU, A CHINESE MANUSCRIPT FROM THE NINTH CENTURY

T hroughout history, desert travelers have told of strange booming noises that seem to be coming right out of the sand itself. Until recently, though, science had no explanation. Now we know that "booming" occurs only in the dozen or so places around the world where a special type of sand grain is found. One such location is Sand Mountain, Nevada, where this recording was made.

Even in these special places, booming occurs only under certain conditions—when the weather and ground are dry, and the sand dune set in motion by wind or some other disturbance. As we discovered in Nevada, the easiest way to start a "booming event" is to climb the dune and then slide back down, inducing the movement of a large volume of sand.

An electron microscope reveals that booming sand grains are fairly round and smooth, as opposed to normal beach-type sand which has irregular features. The cracks and protuberances of normal sand apparently tend to "hook" the grains

OPPOSITE: FLAMINGOS FEED BENEATH SAND DUNES, SANDWICH HARBOR, NAMIBIA.

together when they're sliding downhill. Grains of booming sand, however, cascade down a slope bouncing off each other, transmitting sound energy more easily than normal sand. It's a bit like smooth billiard balls being knocked together, as opposed to fuzzy tennis balls.

Changes in sand temperature may also trigger the phenomenon, as scientists discovered on the moon. During the last *Apollo* mission, geophones (underground microphones) were left behind at the *Apollo 7* site. Researchers monitoring these instruments detected vibrations on the lunar surface at the same time every morning. They were puzzled until someone recalled the phenomenon of earthly booming sands, and reasoned that the vibrations were being generated by slumping lunar soil. Each day as the Sun rose over the lunar surface, the soil went from very cold to very hot. In the process, the top layer of soil would expand and slide just a bit. Given the silence of the lunar surface, even a distant movement could be detected by the geophones.

Booming sands, Namib Desert.

ARCTIC ICE

The polar ice is never still, and I think of the Arctic Ocean in spring as a gigantic jigsaw puzzle forever in motion. —JEAN-LOUIS ETIENNE, FIRST MAN TO REACH THE NORTH POLE SOLO ON SKIS

The variety of ice types and the many patterns of its fracture and dislocation amaze a first-time visitor. What could become as ordinary underfoot as soil or rock remains as exotic as the surface of another planet. —BARRY LOPEZ, *ARCTIC DREAMS*

Ice floes cover thousands of miles in the Arctic Ocean. As these enormous plates of ice move and come in contact with each other, they generate extraordinary sounds like the ones you hear recorded on *Arctic Ice.*

Researcher Robert Asher recorded these sounds somewhere near 80 degrees north latitude, in the Arctic Ocean midway between Barrow, Alaska and Tuktoyaktuk, Canada on the Canadian Abyssal Plain.

As he worked, he tried to forget that the water below was some 12,000 feet deep, while the ice floe he was standing on was half a mile wide and only about a foot thick. It was buckling and overriding an adjacent plate of ice, which produced the sounds you hear. Believe it or not, the total movement of ice during the recording was only about one inch.

As you can imagine, operating sound equipment in the Arctic is no small trick. "I stashed the tape recorder inside my clothes to keep it warm," Asher recalls. "It was under my armpit, beneath six or seven layers of clothing. There

was quite a bit of wind, and it was very, very cold—with the wind chill, around 70 below. Then I'd just stand there with the recorder under my armpit. Now the armpit is the warmest part of the body, and I thought that would keep the recorder warm. Not only didn't it keep it warm enough, the tape recorder motor actually *froze*. So when I say I was cold, I was cold to the core." [21]

ICEBERG AND MIDNIGHT SUN, SOUTH GEORGIA ISLAND.

SOUNDS FROM SPACE

ATMOSPHERIC WHISTLERS

Hear attentively the noise of His voice,
And the sound that goeth out of His mouth.
He sendeth it forth under the whole heaven,
And his lightning unto the ends of the earth.

—JOB 37:2-3

During World War I a German scientist eavesdropping on Allied telephone communications picked up a series of unusual whistling noises. Over the years other scientists observed the same phenomenon, and eventually found a simple explanation for these whistling sounds—lightning.

It's been estimated that lightning flashes somewhere on or above the earth *a hundred times per second.* During each flash the bolt of lightning becomes a short-lived but powerful antenna/transmitter up to a little over a mile long, which broadcasts radio signals in all directions. You most often hear the mid-range frequencies of these signals as static on your car radio.

However, as the German scientist heard, the lightning impulse also generates very-low-frequency (VLF) signals, which can be whisked instantly out into space and back again along the lines of force in Earth's magnetic field. Such signals may travel out into space as far as 16,000 miles before returning to the opposite hemisphere from which they were generated. Their tones seem to "glide" because high frequencies travel faster through the magnetosphere than low fre-

OPPOSITE: LIGHTNING STORM, SEDONA, ARIZONA.

quencies. So when the signal returns from its journey through space, its initial pulse is detected as a longer whistle that descends in pitch.[22] On your recording, the beeps heard at one-second intervals are timing marks.

During its quick detour into space, the whistler also interacts with electrons trapped within Earth's magnetic field. By studying the signal's characteristics (primarily duration and pitch), scientists are able to measure the electron concentration of the atmosphere at great altitudes.

Similarly, scientists are just beginning to understand the dynamic forces controlling the realm of Earth's magnetic influence, or magnetosphere. Surrounding our planet like a cocoon of energy, the magnetosphere acts as a protective buffer between Earth's atmosphere and the "solar wind," the vast storm of subatomic particles and ionized gases emanating from the Sun.

JUPITER CHORUS

… was Jupiter's fire in the thunderbolt—
Or was that tearing noise and flash of light
The storm of winds within the roaring clouds?
What unknown power shakes and splits the earth?
What Law holds stars within their ancient cycles?
—OVID, *THE METAMORPHOSES*, BOOK XV, "THE PHILOSOPHER"

The *Voyager 1* space probe traversed our solar system in the late 1970s armed with an array of sensing devices, including an antenna designed to detect waves of plasma (ionized gas thought to permeate the universe) and low-frequency radio waves. As the spacecraft neared Jupiter in 1979, this antenna picked up the strange signals heard on your recording. Engineers listening on Earth dubbed these signals *Jupiter Chorus* because they sounded like birds singing at dawn.

Like Earth, Jupiter has a magnetic field and magnetosphere which are buffeted by the solar wind.[23] Scientists suspect that the signals in your recording may be plasma waves generated by the solar wind interacting with electrons trapped in Jupiter's magnetosphere. When the solar wind meets Jupiter's magnetic field and the particles trapped within, it is thought to produce an aurora similar to those visible at high latitudes on our planet.

As *Voyager 1* was leaving the Jupiter system, its plasma wave

JOVIAN ATMOSPHERE, JUPITER.

detector picked up something else familiar—faint whistling signals reminiscent of the sounds generated by lightning on Earth (see chapter 28, *Atmospheric Whistlers*). One obvious conclusion—that there is lightning on Jupiter—seems quite fitting on the planet named for the chief god in the Roman pantheon, and the ruler of all celestial phenomena.

AURORA BOREALIS (ALSO THOUGHT TO OCCUR ON JUPITER), ALASKA.

MIRANDA'S MYSTERY

Miranda... What seest thou else
In the dark backward and abysm of time?
If thou rememb'rest aught ere thou camst here
How thou cam'st here thou mayst.
—SHAKESPEARE, *THE TEMPEST*, ACT, 1, SCENE 2

One of the highlights of the *Voyager II* spacecraft's pass near Uranus in 1986 was the remarkable images it made of the planet's five major moons. Especially intriguing was Miranda, a moon 300 miles in diameter, which was named after the character in William Shakespeare's *The Tempest*.

Miranda is a hodgepodge of virtually every geological feature in our solar system: mountains, impact craters, ice flows, and canyons with cliffs rising ten times the height of the walls of the Grand Canyon. The older terrain is full of impact craters that have become softly contoured over time, while the younger terrain has more varied and extreme features. Amidst all this is a vast V-shaped smear, dubbed "the Chevron," which gives Miranda the look of an untidy plaster globe left unfinished by some cosmic sculptor. Its origins are unknown, although scientists speculate that many of Miranda's unusual features may have resulted from internal heating caused by strong gravitational tugs from Uranus and the other moons.

Lost in all the attention paid to *Voyager*'s photographs was the fact that its

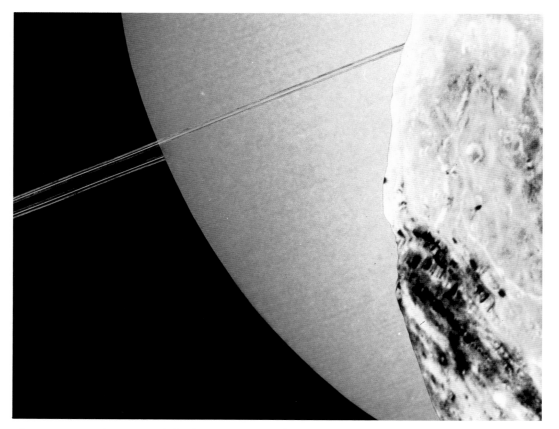

plasma wave detector picked up a series of mysterious signals as the spacecraft neared Miranda. Because the sequence lasted only ten seconds or so, it's repeated several times for you on the CD. And because scientists have no idea yet what the sound represents (a refreshing thought), I've called it *Miranda's Mystery*.

MIRANDA (FOREGROUND) CIRCLING URANUS.

MUSIC OF THE SPHERES

The heavenly motions are nothing but a continuous song for several voices.
—JOHANNES KEPLER, *HARMONICES MUNDI*

The universe itself is said to have been framed by a kind of harmony of sounds, and the heaven itself revolves under the tones of that harmony.
—ISODORE OF SEVILLE (560–636)

German astronomer Johannes Kepler was the first man to accurately describe the motion of planets around the sun. While observing the six planets that were known in his day, Kepler discovered that their orbits were elliptical, not circular. He also calculated, correctly, that the planets speed up as they approach the sun and slow down as they move away.

In his 1619 essay *Harmonices Mundi*, or the "Harmony of the World," he challenged musicians to set his mathematical formulas to music—to realize, in effect, the music of the spheres. Like any periodic motion, he argued, a planet's circumsolar journey could be translated into sound. Further, he imagined this music as a constantly changing symphony—a reflection of his theory, later proven, that the planets will never appear in exactly the same position twice.

It's taken almost 400 years, but the advent of the computer and music synthesizer has made it possible to meet Kepler's challenge.

The sound entitled *Music of the Spheres* is an analog, a manmade sound produced with the help of a music synthesizer. It is, in a sense, a planetarium for the ears, since we "hear" the Solar System from the sun's position at the center, with the planets orbiting around us.

The recording begins with an undulating tone representing Mercury in its elliptical orbit. The variation in pitch corresponds to the change in speed as the planet nears and moves away from the sun. You next hear a tone nearly uniform in pitch, corresponding to the more circular orbit of Venus. We then add the sounds of Earth, Mars, Jupiter, and Saturn, respectively. Because of their relatively slower orbital speeds, Uranus, Neptune, and Pluto are heard as beats rather than tones. Listen with stereo earphones and you'll get the dimensional sense of the planets orbiting around you.

Incidentally, this recording was one of the sounds included in a sound/picture portrait of life on Earth, placed on board the *Voyager* spacecraft in hopes that one day an alien race will find it—the ultimate message in a bottle, adrift in the cosmic ocean. I love the idea of this audio analog of our Solar System whizzing past the objects of its inspiration, beyond the limits of heliocentric imagination, to a new scale of space and sound.

Star trails indicating orbit, Ruth Amphitheater, Alaska.

PULSAR

For we are the stars. For we sing.
For we sing with our light.
For we are birds made of fire.
For we spread our wings over the sky.
Our light is a voice.

—PASSAMAQUODDY INDIAN ("THE STARS")

Much of the exploration of deep space is done using radio telescopes, which detect the radio waves emitted by stars and other heavenly bodies along with visible light.[24] In 1967, when astronomers first discovered a rapidly pulsating radio signal coming from a fixed point in our galaxy, some thought that an extraterrestrial life form was attempting to contact Earth. Further investigation revealed that these pulsing signals were coming from an unusual type of star, which became known as a pulsar.

Pulsars are thought to be neutron stars—remnants of older stars that exploded into supernovas. They are characteristically small—only about ten miles in diameter—and so incredibly dense that a chunk of pulsar the size of a ping-pong ball would weigh a billion tons.

This density makes it possible for the pulsar to rotate furiously. As it does, continuous streams of radio waves are emitted from its magnetic polar regions. And since the magnetic poles are not necessarily located along the star's axis of rotation, beams of the pulsar's radio waves sweep through space like beacons from

OPPOSITE: NORTHWEST QUADRANT OF VELA SUPERNOVA REMNANT.

a lighthouse. Radio telescopes on Earth detect the pulsar's signal-beam as a "blip" every time the star rotates once.

On this recording you'll hear a pulsar that is spinning at a rate of about 11 times a second—slow by pulsar standards. The star's technical name is PSR 0833-45, and it's located in our galaxy near the Vela constellation, approximately 1,500 light-years from Earth.

Some 450 pulsars have been detected to date, although scientists theorize there are probably as many as 100,000 of them in our galaxy. The fastest rotate at a rate of *642 times a second*—much too fast for our ears to discern individual pulses (we hear them instead as a continuous tone).

Several of these speedy "millisecond pulsars" have been discovered. They're so regular in tempo that scientists are experimenting with using these signals as precision timepieces, with each blip of the pulsar representing a unit of time. So far, millisecond pulsars have proven to be at least as precise as our best atomic clocks.

COSMIC BACKGROUND RADIATION

In the beginning Awonawilona (the Creator) was alone. There was nothing beside him in the whole space of time. Everywhere there was black darkness and void. Then Awonawilona conceived in himself the thought, and the thought took shape and went out into the void, into outer space, and from them came nebulae of mist, full of power and growth. —ZUNI CREATION MYTH

Did the universe come into being with a cataclysmic explosion? For years scientists had hypothesized such an origin based on their observations of an expanding universe, whose galaxies are rushing away from each other as if set in motion by a cosmic explosion.

Others countered that if such a "big bang" really happened, then the residual energy generated by it should pervade the cosmos in the form of background radiation.

Such was the state of astronomy one night in April 1965, when physicists Arno Penzias and Robert Wilson of Bell Laboratories were attempting to measure the intensity of radio waves emitted from gases surrounding our galaxy.

Instead they recorded the signal you're listening to, which revealed the presence of microwave radiation coming from all directions in space. These ubiquitous waves were later proven to be the echo of a 15-billion-year-old explosion—physical evidence that the cosmos did indeed begin with a "big bang."[25]

Your recording is the actual signal received on Penzias and Wilson's antenna. Approximately seven percent of the hiss you hear is cosmic background

radiation, energy left over from the big bang. Played through an audio amplifier, the energy is translated into sound, and with a vintage of 15 billion years (give or take five billion), it's the oldest sound you'll ever hear.

I've always liked the idea that this "fossil" sound is essentially what physicists characterize as "white noise." Just as white light includes every color of the rainbow, white noise contains within it all frequencies of sound. Imagine, then, that within this cosmic hiss is hidden every melody ever written, every word ever spoken, every sound that ever was and will be.

GREAT NEBULA IN ORION, A STAR FORMED BY EXPLOSION.

ENDNOTES

"Levels of Listening"

1. This is an oversimplification of one of the more controversial ideas of French audiologist Dr. Alfred Tomatis. He suggests that there are certain frequencies (between 2,000 to 3,000 hz and higher) which in effect help "charge the brain" with energy and vitality. Dr. Tomatis has found these frequencies especially prevalent in Gregorian chant and the music of Mozart. According to Dr. Tomatis, low frequencies—such as those emphasized in the bass component of rock-'n'-roll music—tend to drain and devitalize our mental energies. The English translation of Dr. Tomatis' book, *The Conscious Ear*, is available from Station Hill Press, Barrytown, NY 12507. Also highly recommended is *When Listening Comes Alive*, by Paul Madaule, from Moulin Publishing, P.O. Box 560, Norval, Ontario, Canada L0P 1K0.

2. The findings of psychologist James J. Lynch are discussed in his book, *The Language of the Heart: The Human Body in Dialogue*, published by Basic Books, 1986. See also *Journal of Medical Science*, 1982, Vol. 18, pp. 575-579; *Science News*, February 26, 1986, and *Integrative Physiological and Behavioral Science*, April-June 1992, Vol. 27, No. 2, pp. 151-169.

3. There are many variations on this theme: you can imagine yourself in the center of an expanding bubble, listening to all the sounds along its periphery. You can try increasing the size of the circle or bubble. Paul Madaule details some listening exercises in his book (see footnote #1). R. Murray Schafer's *A Sound Education* (available from Arcana Editions, Indian River, Ontario, Canada K0L 2B0) is a veritable cornucopia of what he calls "ear-cleaning exercises." Schafer's *Tuning of the World*, also available from Arcana, is the classic text on soundscape theory. He's done more than anyone else I know to turn people on to the idea and practice of listening. A word of caution: there are some good reasons why we've become habitually desensitized to sound. Urban environments can be audio garbage bins where noise pollution is the rule. Circumventing our protective hearing mechanism opens us not only to the "good" sounds, but to the bad and the ugly as well. Sound is a powerful medium indeed, and we should always, particularly when in a vulnerable or relatively open state, be mindful of where we are and what we're choosing to listen to.

4. At the very least, we can hear the intonation and rhythm of her voice in the womb. The uterine environment filters out the voice's upper frequencies; however, it's been shown that newborn infants respond more to the sound of their mother's voice than any other female voice. They also seem to prefer the sound of their mother's voice to silence. (Source: Christine Moon, Assistant Professor of Psychology, Pacific Lutheran University.)

5. Try this experiment: imagine speaking your name out loud, and see if you can hear the sound of it in your "mind's ear." Then try saying it aloud, and compare the way you preheard it with what actually comes out. I find that I don't quite know how my voice will sound; I'm surprised by it. What does seem familiar about "my" voice is the sensation of it, and the places and textures of vibrations as I speak.

6. We've learned, unconsciously, to use the sound of someone's voice to gauge whether or not we believe them. (See "Effects of Pitch and Speech Rate on Personal Attributions," by William Apple, Robert Krauss, and Lynn A. Streeter in the *Journal of Personality and Social Psychology*, 1979, Vol. 37, No. 5, pp. 714-727.) Western society has come to associate truth and trust with a deep bass voice and falsehood with a higher "falsetto" voice. A quick listen to the evening news will demonstrate that this vocal trait has been co-opted by TV and radio announcers—me too! We're struck not so much by what he or she is saying, but by the authority connoted in their tone of voice.

During World War II, a blind man named Jacques Lusseyran came to be a leader in the French resistance. One of his responsibilities was to screen new candidates for entry into the clandestine organization. Lusseyran could tell infallibly whether anyone was telling the truth or not by carefully listening to the sound of their voice. "The human voice forces its way into us," he later explained. "It's really inside ourselves that we hear it. To hear (someone else's voice) properly, we must allow it to vibrate in our heads and our chests, in our throats, as if for the moment it really belonged to us. That is surely why voices never deceive us." Jacques Lusseyran, *And There Was Light*, 1987. Parabola Books, New York.

7. Wei Ying-wu, "On Sound," translated by Irving Y. Lo, 1990. *Sunflower Splendor*, Indiana University Press, Bloomington; reprinted with permission from the translator and slightly revised by him.

8. In a speech given at the "Tuning of the World Conference," in Banff, Alberta, Canada, 1993.

"Pulse of the Planet"

1. Didier Demolin, "The Social Organization of Mangbetu Music," in *African Reflections: Art from Northeastern Zaire*, 1990, Enid Schildkrout and Curtis A. Keim, eds., pp.# 195-208, New York and Seattle, American Museum of Natural History and University of Washington Press.

2. George A. Schweinfurth, *The Heart of Africa: Three Years' Travels and Adventures in the Unexplored Regions of Central Africa from 1868-1871*, 1874, 2 vols., translated by Ellen E. Frewer; New York, Harper & Brothers.

3. Louis Sarno, from an interview with the author.

4. Donald Tuzin, "Miraculous Voices: The Auditory Experience of Numinous Objects," *Current Anthropology*, December 1984, vol. 25, No. 5. Professor Tuzin poses

the question: what happens when we are exposed to low-frequency vibrations which our brain detects but can't identify? Cattle and other animals have often been observed to grow uneasy before a thunderstorm or an earthquake. Are they demonstrating a sensitivity to the infrasonic vibrations being generated? Are humans susceptible to low-frequency sounds? Could an anxiety reaction be stimulated by the infrasonic component of a bullroarer? Professor Tuzin suggests that the low frequencies generated by the bullroarers help establish an aura of mystery and awe—elements crucial to the impact of the ritual event.

5. Huston Smith, "Unique Vocal Abilities of Certain Tibetan Lamas," *American Anthropologist*, 1967, Vol. 69, No. 2.

6. The Venerable Abbot Konchuk Wangdu, in an interview with the author, stated: "There's no question from our experience that the sound of these chants, this ancient sacred sound … will be definitely beneficial … if the listener has a kind of faith, a sense of trust that this is something done by religious persons who have the welfare of living beings at heart. When approached in that way, whether the person understands it or not, it will have some sort of transforming effect on the mind of the person. The more knowledge a person has (mantra practice, visualization mastery, and knowledge of the neural system) the more benefit it has. The sound itself carries the insight, and people react in the way they

do." (Special thanks to Robert Thurman, translator. For more of this interview, see *Parabola Magazine*, Spring 1989, Vol. XIV, No. 2, "Chanted Blessings in Disguise.")

7. Donations for the support of this cause can be made to the Society for Gyutö Sacred Arts, Box 358, San Rafael, CA 94915.

8. For more information on trekking and environmental awareness, see "Himalaya Ecotravel," *Buzzworm, The Environmental Journal*, May/June 1993, or write The Kathmandu Environmental Education Project (KEEP), P.O. Box 4944, Tridevi Marg, Thamel, Kathmandu, Nepal; or The Annapurna Conservation Area Project (ACAP), c/o King Mahendra Trust, Jawalekhel, P.O. Box 3712, Kathmandu, Nepal.

9. From an interview with the author. Professor Wilson is considered the world's foremost authority on ants and was the recipient, with Bert Hölldobler, of the Pulitzer Prize for the book *The Ants*.

10. Given the damage that these insect pests inflict on the annual rice crop, it's not surprising that the Japanese have pioneered in leafhopper research. The technique for recording the insect songs with the use of a recording stylus was developed by T. Ichikawa, M. Sakuma, and S. Ishii; see *Applied Entomology and Zoology*, 1975, Vol. 10, pp. 162-171. Applied Entomology and Zoology, c/o Japan Plant Protection Association, 1-43-11 Komagone, Todhima-ku, Tokyo 170, Japan.

11. Termites are not ants. They're generally thought to have evolved from an animal similar to a cockroach (entomologist Edward O. Wilson refers to them as "social cockroaches"). Nevertheless, over millions of years, both ants and termites have independently evolved remarkably similar social systems.

12. The frequency of sound is measured in cycles per second, or hertz (hz). The range of human hearing extends from 20 to 20,000 hz, with most of what humans hear taking place below 10,000 hz. Bat echolocation signals may be as high as 70,000 hz.

13. For more information about these remarkable, beneficial creatures, contact Bat Conservation International, P.O. Box 162603, Austin, TX 78716.

14. In the Scandinavian Volsung saga, for example, when Sigurd slays the dragon Fafnir and tastes its blood, he suddenly finds he can understand the conversation of a flock of nearby birds.

15. Many species of birds (redstarts, blackbirds, starlings, and mockingbirds, to name a few) are able to successfully mimic the calls of other species. Australia's lyrebird is famous for its uncanny imitations. Reputedly, it even does renditions of human sounds, such as chain saws! The reason for the mimicry is one of the many unanswered questions in the study of bird song. There are some remarkable similarities between how birds learn their songs and how humans learn to speak a language. See Peter Marler, "Birdsong and Speech Development: Could There Be Parallels?" *American Scientist*, November-December 1970, Vol. 58, No. 6, pp. 669-673.

16. Like the human voice, an elephant vocalization is a blend, a composite, of many sounds of different frequencies. Some of these component sounds we humans can hear, and some (the infrasounds) we can't. The elephant repertory includes vocalizations that are relatively strong in high frequencies—the famous "trumpet call" is a good example. At the other end of the spectrum are the predominantly infrasonic rumbles on our recording. They have some component frequencies in the low end of our audible range, which is why we can hear them, barely, if they are intense enough and we are close enough. When we speed up the recording, the sounds appear to be richer and more complex. The previously inaudible portions of the elephant's voice are now within our range.

17. Carlton Ray; William A. Watkins; John J. Burns, "The Underwater Song of *Erignathus* (Bearded Seal)," *Zoologica: The New York Zoological Society*, 1969, Vol. 54, No. 2, pp. 79-86.

18. Philip N. Lehner, "Coyote Vocalizations: A Lexicon and Comparisons with Other Canids," *Animal Behavior*, 1978, Vol. 26, pp. 712-722.

19. Dr. Bernard Grzimek, ed., *Grzimek's Animal Life Encyclopedia*, New York, Van Nostrand Reinhold Company.

20. Roy T. Arnold, Henry E. Bass, and Lee N. Bolen, "Acoustical Spectral Analysis of Three Tornadoes," *Journal of the Acoustical Society of America*, 1976, Vol. 60, No. 3, pp. 584-593.

21. Robert Asher, Research Associate and Scientific Advisor, Glaciological and Arctic Sciences Institute, from an interview with the author.

22. Whistlers can be picked up on an ordinary amplifier connected to a long wire antenna. An important condition for monitoring whistler activity is a low noise level, which means rural areas tend to be best. Polar regions are particularly suitable for whistler research.

23. Jupiter's magnetic field is much more powerful than Earth's. In fact, Jupiter's magnetosphere, the largest "object" in the Solar System, stretches all the way from Jupiter to Saturn. For more information on Earth's magnetosphere, see "Atmospheric Whistlers," chapter #28.

24. Most stars emit light waves; the exceptions are called black holes. Many stars, including pulsars, also emit radio waves strong enough to be detected on Earth by radio telescopes.

25. Penzias and Wilson received the 1978 Nobel Prize in Physics for their work.

CREDITS

THE TEXT

1) WATER DRUMMING: Lord Byron quoted by Edward Lee, *Music of the People: A Study of Popular Music in Great Britain*, 1970, Barrie and Jenkins. 2) BAYAKA SONG: Cedric Wright quoted in *Earth Prayers From Around the World: 365 Prayers, Poems and Invocations for Honoring the Earth*, 1991, Elizabeth Roberts and Elias Amidon, eds., Harper, San Francisco. 3) KALULI SONG: Steven Feld from an interview with the author. 4) INITIA-TION RITE: Male cult myth retold by Donald Tuzin from an interview with the author. 5) TIBETAN CHANT: Venerable Abbot Konchuk Wangdu from an inter-view conducted with the author. Special thanks to Robert Thurman, translator. For more of this interview, see footnote #6. 6) SIBERIAN SHAMANS: Shaman of the Tungus people, quoted by Lev Iakovlevich Schternberg in "Shamanism and Religious Election," *Introduction to Soviet Ethnology*, 1974, Vol. 1, Stephen P. Dunn and Ethel Dunn, eds.; Highgate Road Social Science Research Station. 7) NEPALESE CARA-VAN: Peter Matthiessen, *The Snow Leopard*, 1978, Viking Penguin, a division of Penguin Books USA, Inc, New York. 8) ANTS: Black Elk quoted by Joseph Epes Brown in "The Bison and the Moth: Lakota Correspon-dences," *Parabola*, May 1983, Vol. VIII, No. 2. 9) LEAFHOPPERS: Shiki from *Haiku Harvest*, P. Beilenson and H. Behn, eds., 1962, Peter Pauper Press, Mt. Vernon, New York. 10) TERMITES: Richard Lydekker, ed., *Library of Natural History*, 1904, Saal-field Publishing Co., New York; pp. 31-40.

11) BATS: Randall Jarrell, "Bats," from *The Bat-Poet*, 1964, Macmillan Publishing Co. 12) BIRD SONG: Hal Borland, *Twelve Moons of the Year*, 1979, Alfred A. Knopf, New York. 13) ELEPHANTS: Heathcote Williams, *Sacred Elephant*, 1989, Harmony Books, a division of Crown Publishers, Inc. 14) BEARDED SEALS: Netsilik Eskimo prayer from *Songs and Stories of the Netsilik Eskimos*, translated by Edward Fields from text collected by Knud Rasmussen, courtesy Educational Development Center Inc., Newton, Massachusetts. 15) COYOTES: Hopi story adapted from "Why Coyote Howls at the Sky," in Rosalind Kerven's *Earth Magic, Sky Magic*, 1991, Cambridge University Press, New York. 16) COLO-BUS MONKEYS: East African myth adapted from "The Monkey Princes," in Eleanor B. Heady's *Safiri the Singer*, Follett Publishing Company, Chicago. 17) GIB-BONS: Shen Yüeh, R. H. Van Gulik, *The Gibbon in China: An Essay in Chinese Animal Lore*, 1967, E. J. Brill, Leiden, Holland. 18) OROPENDOLA BIRD: Henry Walter Bates, *The Naturalist on the River Amazons*, 1989, Penguin Books, New York; first pub-lished in 1863. 21) SUIKINKUTSU: Buson from R. H. Blyth, *Haiku*, Vol. III, 1952, Charles E. Tuttle Co., Inc., Rutland, Vermont. 22) AEOLIAN HARP: Eduard Mörike, 19th-century German poet, from "To An Aeolian Harp." 23) TORNADO: Witness to a tornado quoted in "Monthly Weather Review," 1930, Vol. 58, No. 205. 24) EARTHQUAKE: James Audubon quoted by William Corliss, *Earthquakes, Tides, Unidentified Sounds and Related Phenomena*, 1983, The Sourcebook Project,

Glen Arm, Maryland. Audubon's account refers to what is now called the New Madrid Earthquakes, which devastated the Missouri countryside in 1811 and 1812. 26) BOOM-ING SANDS: Tun Huang Lu from Marquess Curzon of Kedleston's, *Tales of Travel*, 1923, Hodder and Stoughton, London. 27) ARC-TIC ICE: Jean-Louis Etienne, *National Geographic*, September 1986, Vol. 170, No. 3. Barry Lopez, *Arctic Dreams*, 1986, Charles Scribner's Sons, an imprint of Macmillan Publishing Co., New York. 29) JUPITER CHORUS: Publius Ovidius Naso, *The Metamorphoses*, trans. by Horace Gregory, 1958, Viking Penguin, a division of Penguin Books USA, Inc., New York. 32) PULSAR: Passamaquoddy Indian from Jerome Rothen-berg's "The Stars," *Technicians of the Sacred*, 1968, Doubleday & Co., New York. 33) COSMIC BACKGROUND RADIA-TION: Zuni creation myth, Marie-Louise von Franz, *Patterns of Creativity Mirrored in Creation Myths*, 1972, Spring Publications, Dallas, Texas.

THE RECORDINGS

1) WATER DRUMMING: Didier Demolin, Department of General Linguistics, University of Brussels, Belgium. If you're interested in hearing more music of the Mangbetu people, Fonti Musicali has released a CD entitled "Mangbetu-Zaire: Haut-Uele" (fmd 193), available from Qualiton Import, Ltd., 2402 40th Ave., Long Island City, NY, 11101. 2) BAYAKA SONG: Louis Sarno. See his book, *Song From the Forest: My Life Among*

the Ba-Benjellé Pygmies, 1993, published by Houghton Mifflin, New York. 3) KALULI SONG: Edited from a radio production by Scott Sinkler and Steven Feld called "Voices in the Forest." Original recording by Feld, 1982. For more music and environmental sound from the land of the Kaluli, listen to "Voices of the Rainforest" (RCD 10173), a CD available from Rykodisc, Pickering Wharf, Bldg. C, Salem, MA, 01970. 4) INITIATION RITE: Courtesy of Donald Tuzin, Professor of Anthropology, UC San Diego. 5) TIBETAN CHANT: Mickey Hart, 360° Productions, and the Gyutö Monks. Recordings currently available include "The Gyutö Monks Tantric Choir," Windham Hill WD-2001; "The Gyutö Monks, Freedom Chants From the Roof of the World," Rykodisc RCD20113 (for address see credit #3). 6) SIBERIAN SHAMANS: Recorded by Waldemar Jochelson during the Jesup Expedition (1897–1902). Courtesy of the Department of Anthropology, American Museum of Natural History (special thanks to Tom Miller and Belinda Kaye), and Marilyn Graf at the Archives of Traditional Music, Indiana University. 7) NEPALESE CARAVAN: Jim Metzner. For an account of the trek, see East West Journal, August and September, 1983. 8) ANTS: Bernie Krause. © 1993 Wild Sanctuary Music. All rights reserved. For more information, write Wild Sanctuary, 13012 Henno Rd., Glen Ellen, CA, 95442. 9) LEAF-HOPPERS: Dr. Peter Stiling, Assistant Professor, Department of Biology, University of South Florida.

10) TERMITES: Louis Sarno. (See also #2.) 11) BATS: Recorded under the direction of Dr. William O'Neill at Rochester University's Center for Brain Research. 12) BIRD SONG: Crawford Greenewalt, courtesy of the Cornell Laboratory of Ornithology. 13) ELE-PHANTS: Zita's calls were recorded by Katharine Payne and Joyce Poole. The other selection was recorded by William Langbauer, Katy Payne, and their research team, courtesy Cornell's Bioacoustics Research Program. For more information on elephant communication research, contact the Amboseli Elephant Research Project, c/o Kenya Wildlife Service, P.O. Box 48177, Nairobi, Kenya. 14) BEARD-ED SEALS: Christopher W. Clark, Director of the Bioacoustics Research Program, Cornell Laboratory of Ornithol-ogy. For more sounds of seals and their neighbors, listen to "Ocean Voices of the Alaskan Arctic," available from the Cornell Laboratory of Ornithology, 159 Sapsucker Woods Road, Ithaca, NY, 14850-1999. 15) COYOTES: Fred and Ginny Trumbull, who have been recording nature sounds since 1950. 16) COLOBUS MONKEYS: Douglas Quin, award-winning composer and wildlife recordist. 17) GIBBONS: The solo male gibbon was recorded in 1986 at the Gunung Palung Nature Reserve, West Kalimantan, Indonesia, by John Mitani, Associate Professor, Department of Anthropology, University of Michigan. The female's great call was recorded in Kalimantan, Borneo, by Ruth Happel, President of Animal InterActive Arts, Pittsboro, North Carolina. Ruth's record-

ings have been released on both the Wild Sanctuary and Rykodisc labels (see credits #3 and #8 for addresses). 18) OROPEN-DOLA BIRD: Douglas Quin. (See also #16.) 19) JAPANESE DEER: Jim Metzner. 20) SHISHI ODOSHI: Jim Metzner. 21) SUIKINKUTSU: Yu Wakao, Assistant Professor, Hiroshima University. The recording is a montage of sounds from three suikinkutsus: the Takashima house in Obama City, Fukui prefecture; Hojuin Temple in Kira-cho, Aichi prefecture; and the Nakamura house in Kyoto. 22) AEOLIAN HARP: Jim Metzner. Harp constructed by Paul Dixon. 23) TORNADO: Courtesy of Richard Alan Lindley and Dr. Henry Bass, Department of Physics and Astronomy, University of Mississippi. 24) EARTH-QUAKE: Dr. Brian Jacob, Institute of Advanced Studies, Dublin, Ireland. Thanks also to Neil Conan of National Public Radio. 25) LAVA FLOW: Doug Hodge, sound recordist specializing in volcanoes and things Hawaiian. 26) BOOMING SANDS: Sand Mountain's sands were recorded in stereo by Bernie Krause, Wild Sanctuary. Stereo booming sand recordings © 1993 Wild Sanctuary Music. All rights reserved. Monaural recordings courtesy of David Criswell, Director, Institute of Space Systems Operations, University of Houston, Texas. 27) ARCTIC ICE: Recorded by Robert Asher, Research Associate and Scientific Advisor, Glaciological and Arctic Sciences Institute. 28) ATMOSPHERIC WHISTLERS: Made at Vandenberg Air Force Base, 1960. Provided by Robert Helliwell, Professor Emeritus, Electrical

Engineering, Stanford University. 29 & 30) JUPITER CHORUS and MIRANDA'S MYSTERY: Fred Scarf, principal investigator of plasma-wave research on many space flights, including *Voyager*'s. 31) MUSIC OF THE SPHERES: Willie Ruff, Associate Professor, Yale School of Music, and John Rodgers, Silliman Professor of Geology, Yale University. They've produced a full-length recording of "The Harmony of the World." For further information, contact The Kepler Label, P.O. Box 1779, New Haven, CT 06507. 32) PULSAR: Courtesy of Richard N. Manchester, Australia Telescope National Facility. Recorded in 1975, Green Bank Radio Telescope, West Virginia. 33) COSMIC BACKGROUND RADIATION: Robert Wilson and Arno Penzias. Recorded at Bell Laboratories, Holmdel, New Jersey.

The *Pulse of the Planet* CD was mixed on a digital work station using Digidesign's Protools.™

THE PHOTOGRAPHY AND ILLUSTRATIONS

Page 2: Robert Asher/Foundation for Glacier and Environmental Research; **page 5**: Robb Kendrick; **page 6**: Annie Griffiths Belt; **page 9**: Dolores Metzner; **page 10**: Peter Menzel; **page 12**: © Hans Jenny. Contact MACROmedia, Epping, N.H.; **page 15**: Lennart Nilsson, *A Child Is Born*, Dell Publishing; **page 18**: James L.

Stanfield, © National Geographic Society; **page 21**: Robb Kendrick; **page 22**: Didier Demolin; **page 24**: Frans Lanting/Minden Pictures; **page 26**: Michael Nichols/Magnum; **page 28**: Steven Feld; **page 30**: G. B. McIntosh; **page 31**: Malcolm Kirk; **page 33**: Courtesy of the monks of Gyütö; **pages 34-35**: Robb Kendrick; **page 37**: Courtesy Department of Library Services/American Museum of Natural History; **page 40**: Robb Kendrick; **page 41**: Annie Griffiths Belt; **page 43**: Mark Moffet/Minden Pictures; **page 44**: Don & Pat Valenti/DRK PHOTO; **page 48**: Frans Lanting/Minden Pictures; **page 50**: Stephen J. Krasemann/DRK PHOTO; **page 51**: Merlin D. Tuttle/Bat Conservation International; **page 53**: A.& E. Morris/VIREO; **page 54**: John Mitani; **page 56**: Robert Caputo/Aurora; **page 59**: Wayne Lynch/DRK PHOTO; **page 62**: Barbara Gerlach/DRK PHOTO; **page 65**: Stephen J. Krasemann/DRK PHOTO; **page 67**: Frans Lanting/Minden Pictures; **page 69**: John Cancalosi/DRK PHOTO; **page 70**: Kiyoshi Sakamoto, © National Geographic Society; **pages 71 and 72**: Michael S. Yamashita; **page 73**: G. B. McIntosh; **page 74**: Michael S. Yamashita; **page 75**: G. B. McIntosh; **page 76**: Fran Durner/The Anchorage Daily News; **page 77**: Annie Griffiths Belt; **page 78**: Peter Willing; **page 82**: Carl Mydans/Life Magazine © Time Warner Inc.; **page 83**: Peter French/DRK PHOTO; **pages 84-85**: Chris Johns; **pages 86 and 88**: Annie Griffiths Belt; **page 90**: Frans Lanting/Minden Pictures; **pages 91 and 92**: Warren Faidley/Weatherstock; **pages 94-95**: NASA; **page 96**: Johnny

Johnson/DRK PHOTO; **page 98**: NASA; **pages 100-101**: Kennan Ward/DRK PHOTO; **page 102**: David Malin, © ROE/AAT Board, Anglo-Australian Observatory; **page 106**: David Malin, Courtesy of Anglo-Australian Observatory.

ACKNOWLEDGMENTS

To my wife Dolores and daughter Sarah, who have had to put up with many days (and nights) of Dad working away in his studio, fine-tuning tornadoes; to the scientists whom I've had the privilege of interviewing; to the sound recordists who have given their talents to my radio series and this compact disk and book; to Andy Cary, for his help and equanimity; to Cathy Kouts of the Nature Company, for believing in this project and seeing it through; to Carolyn Clark and Don Belt for their patience; to Dick Woodward and Jamie Murray of the DuPont Company, for their continuing support; to Shana Chrystie, Timothy Ferris, David Freudberg, Karl Karst, Clay Reeves, Gary Schonfeld, Hans Werner, and Tim Wilson, for their friendship and good advice; to Jean and Jerry, who I wish were here to hold this in their hands.
—*Jim Metzner*

As we prepare for a possible sequel to this publication, I'd like to invite readers/listeners to send suggestions and ideas for new sounds to: Jim Metzner, P.O. Box 22, Croton-on-Hudson, NY 10520.